CAP 413

Radiotelephony manual

Civil Aviation Authority London April 1984

© Civil Aviation Authority 1984

ISBN 0 86039 199 X

First published September 1978
Reprinted January 1979
Reprinted October 1979
Second edition April 1984
Reprinted September 1984
Reprinted with corrections June 1986

Printed and distributed by
Civil Aviation Authority, Greville House, 37 Gratton Road, Cheltenham, England

FOREWORD

STATUS

This publication is based on the International Standards and Recommended Practices contained in ICAO Annex 10 Volume 2 (Communications Procedures) to the Convention on International Civil Aviation and the PANS-RAC (Procedures for Air Navigation Services, Rules of the Air and Air Traffic Services) Doc 4444–RAC/501/11.

It is a useful reference book for the examination for the flight Radiotelephony Operators (Restricted) Licence, details of which are contained in CAP 90, current operational details are to be found in the United Kingdom AIP. However, air traffic controllers, aerodrome flight information officers and aeronautical radio station operators should refer to MATS Pt 1, MAFIS (CAP 410) and Operators' Guide (CAP 452) respectively for comprehensive instructions on phraseology to be used by aeronautical ground radio stations.

FORMAT

The examples of phraseology in this handbook are intended to be representative of radiotelephony procedures in common use. The initial call in a series of messages always appears on the left hand side of the page. The remaining messages connected with the subject of the initial call appear in chronological order on the right hand side.

The agency making the transmission is identified by the colour background of the example phraseology, as follows:

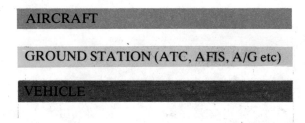

AIRCRAFT

GROUND STATION (ATC, AFIS, A/G etc)

VEHICLE

While the procedures and phraseologies specifically reflect the situation in an environment where Very High Frequency (VHF) is in use, they are equally applicable in those areas where High Frequency (HF) is used.

In the latter case a strict adherence to procedures is considered essential because of the greater interference potential and in many cases poor reception resulting from the propagation characteristics of certain frequency bands.

All enquiries regarding the text of this publication are to be addressed to:

> Head of C(AP)3
> Room T1027
> CAA House
> 45–59 Kingsway
> London WC2B 6TE

TABLE OF CONTENTS

Chapter 1   – GLOSSARY   1
     1.1 – Definitions of principal terms used in this manual   1
     1.2 – Commonly used abbreviations   4
     1.3 – Hours of service and communications watch   6
     1.4 – Record of communications   6
     1.5 – Categories of message   7

Chapter 2   – GENERAL OPERATING PROCEDURES   9
     2.1 – Introduction   9
     2.2 – Transmitting technique   9
     2.3 – Transmission of letters   10
     2.4 – Transmission of numbers   11
     2.5 – Transmission of time   13
     2.6 – Standard words and phrases   14
     2.7 – Communications   16
     2.8 – Military Aerodrome Traffic Zones and associated
         penetration service   26
     2.9 – Lower Airspace Radar Advisory Service   27
     2.10 – Pilots complaints concerning aeronautical
         communications   27
     2.11 – Air Traffic Service complaints about pilot
         communications   28

Chapter 3   – GENERAL PHRASEOLOGY   29
     3.1 – Introduction   29
     3.2 – Level instructions   29
     3.3 – Position reporting   31
     3.4 – Flight plans   32

Chapter 4   – AERODROME AIR TRAFFIC SERVICES: AIRCRAFT   33
    4.1   – Introduction   33
    4.2   – Type of service   33
    4.3   – Departure information and engine starting procedures   34
    4.4   – Pushback   35
    4.5   – Taxi instructions   35
    4.6   – Pre-departure manoeuvring   38
    4.7   – Take-off procedures   38
    4.8   – Aerodrome traffic circuit   43
    4.9   – Final approach and landing   45
    4.10   – Go around   48
    4.11   – After landing   49
    4.12   – Essential aerodrome information   50

Chapter 5   – AERODROME AIR TRAFFIC SERVICES: VEHICLES   51
    5.1   – Introduction   51
    5.2   – Movement instructions   51
    5.3   – Crossing runways   53
    5.4   – Vehicles towing aircraft   54

Chapter 6   – GENERAL RADAR PHRASEOLOGY   57
    6.1   – Introduction   57
    6.2   – Radar identification and vectoring   57
    6.3   – Secondary Surveillance Radar   58
    6.4   – Radar Control   60
    6.5   – Radar vectoring   60
    6.6   – Traffic information and avoiding action   61
    6.7   – Radar assistance to aircraft with radio-communications
         failure   63

Chapter 7   – APPROACH CONTROL   65
    7.1   – IFR departures   65
    7.2   – VFR departures   66
    7.3   – IFR arrivals   66
    7.4   – VFR arrivals   72
    7.5   – Special VFR flights   74
    7.6   – Radar vectors to final approach   75
    7.7   – QGH Procedure   78
    7.8   – Surveillance radar approach   81

Chapter 8 – AREA CONTROL   85
       8.1 – Area control units   85
       8.2 – Position information   85
       8.3 – Level information   86
       8.4 – Flights joining airways   87
       8.5 – Flights leaving airways   88
       8.6 – Flights crossing airways   89
       8.7 – Flights holding en-route   89

Chapter 9 – DISTRESS AND URGENCY PROCEDURES   91
       9.1 – Introduction   91
       9.2 – VHF Emergency service   91
       9.3 – Distress   92
       9.4 – Urgency   96
       9.5 – Difficulty   98
       9.6 – Practice emergencies   98

Chapter 10 – TRANSMISSION OF AERODROME INFORMATION   99
       10.1 – Meteorological information   99
       10.2 – Runway Visual Range (RVR)   99
       10.3 – Runway surface conditions   100

Chapter 11 – MISCELLANEOUS FLIGHT HANDLING   101
       11.1 – Wake turbulence   101
       11.2 – Wind shear   101
       11.3 – Direction finding   101
       11.4 – Airmiss reporting   102
       11.5 – Oil pollution reporting   103
       11.6 – Interceptions by military aircraft   104
       11.7 – Aircraft operating agency messages   104

CHAPTER 1–GLOSSARY

1.1   DEFINITIONS

Aerodrome control service Air traffic control service for aerodrome traffic.

Aerodrome traffic All traffic on the manoeuvring area of an aerodrome and all aircraft operating in the vicinity of an aerodrome.

Aeronautical mobile service A radio communication service between aircraft stations and aeronautical stations, or between aircraft stations.

Aeronautical station A land station in the aeronautical mobile service. In certain instances, an aeronautical station may be placed on board a ship or an earth satellite.

Aircraft station A mobile station in the aeronautical mobile service on board an aircraft.

Air-ground communications Two-way communication between aircraft and stations or locations on the surface of the earth.

Air traffic All aircraft in flight or operating on the manoeuvring area of an aerodrome.

Air traffic services A generic term meaning variously, flight information service, alerting service, air traffic advisory service, air traffic control service, area control service, approach control service or aerodrome control service.

Altitude The vertical distance of a level, a point or an object considered as a point, measured from mean sea level.

Area control centre A unit established to provide air traffic control service to controlled flights in control areas under its jurisdiction.

Automatic terminal information service The provision of current, routine information to arriving and departing aircraft by means of continuous and repetitive broadcasts throughout the day or a specified portion of the day.

Blind transmission A transmission from one station to another station in circumstances where two-way communication cannot be established but where it is believed that the called station is able to receive the transmission.

Broadcast A transmission of information relating to air navigation that is not addressed to a specific station or stations.

Clearance limit The point to which an aircraft is granted an air traffic control clearance.

Expected approach time The time at which ATC expects that an arriving aircraft, following a delay, will leave the holding point to complete its approach for a landing.

Flight level A surface of constant atmospheric pressure, which is related to a specific pressure datum, 1013.2 mb, and is separated from other such surfaces by specific pressure intervals.

Flight plan Specified information provided to air traffic services units, relative to an intended flight or portion of a flight of an aircraft.

Heading The direction in which the longitudinal axis of an aircraft is pointed, usually expressed in degrees from North (true, magnetic, compass or grid).

Height The vertical distance of a level, a point, or an object considered as a point measured from a specified datum.

IFR flight A flight conducted in accordance with the instrument flight rules.

Instrument meteorological conditions Meteorological conditions expressed in terms of visibility, horizontal and vertical distance from cloud less than the minima specified for visual meteorological conditions.

Level A generic term relating to the vertical position of an aircraft in flight and meaning variously, height, altitude or flight level.

Missed approach procedure The procedure to be followed if, after an approach, a landing is not effected.

Radar vectoring Provision of navigational guidance to aircraft in the form of specific headings, based on the use of radar.

Reporting point A specified geographical location at which the position of an aircraft is reported.

Runway visual range The range over which the pilot of an aircraft on the centre line of a runway can see the runway surface markings or the lights delineating the runway or identifying its centre line.

VFR flight A flight conducted in accordance with the visual flight rules.

Visual meteorological conditions Meteorological conditions expressed in terms of visibility, distance from cloud, and ceiling, equal to or better than specified minima.

Note: Other definitions will be found in the appropriate documents.

1.2 COMMONLY USED ABBREVIATIONS

1.2.1 The abbreviations annotated with an asterisk are normally spoken as complete words. The remainder are normally spoken using the constituent letters rather than the spelling alphabet.

ACC	Area control centre
ADF	Automatic direction-finding equipment
ADR	Advisory route
ADT	Approved departure time
AFIS*	Aerodrome flight information service
AFTN	Aeronautical fixed telecommunication network
AGL	Above ground level
AIC	Aeronautical information circular
AIP	Aeronautical information publication
AIS	Aeronautical information services
AMSL	Above mean sea level
ATC	Air traffic control (in general)
ATCC	Air Traffic Control Centre
ATD	Actual time of departure
ATIS*	Automatic terminal information service
ATS	Air traffic services
ATSU	Air Traffic Services Unit
ATZ	Aerodrome traffic zone
CAVOK*	Visibility, cloud and present weather better than prescribed values or conditions (CAVOK pronounced Cav-okay)
CTR	Control zone
DME	Distance measuring equipment
EAT	Expected approach time
EET	Estimated elapsed time
ETA	Estimated time of arrival or estimating arrival
ETD	Estimated time of departure or estimating departure

FIR	Flight information region
FIS	Flight information service
H24	Continuous day and night service (H24 pronounced Aitch Twenty Fower)
IFR	Instrument flight rules
ILS	Instrument landing system
IMC	Instrument meteorological conditions
MATZ*	Military Aerodrome Traffic Zone
MET*	Meteorological or meteorology
NDB	Non-directional radio beacon
OAC	Oceanic area control centre
OCA	Oceanic control area
PAPIS*	Precision approach path indicating system (PAPIS pronounced Pa-pee)
QDM	Magnetic heading (zero wind) . . .
QFE	Atmospheric pressure at aerodrome elevation (or at runway threshold)
QGH	Letdown procedure using VDF equipment
QNH	Altimeter sub-scale setting to obtain elevation when on the ground
QTE	True bearing
RCC	Rescue co-ordination centre
RTF	Radiotelephone
RVR	Runway visual range
SID*	Standard instrument departure
SIGMET*	Significant information concerning en-route weather phenomena which may affect the safety of aircraft operations
SSR	Secondary surveillance radar
STAR*	Standard (instrument) arrival route
TAF*	Aerodrome forecast

TMA	Terminal control area
UIR	Upper flight information region
UTC	Co-ordinated Universal Time
VASIS*	Visual approach slope indicator system (VASIS pronounced Var-zi)
VDF	Very high frequency direction-finding station
VFR	Visual flight rules
VHF	Very high frequency (30 to 300 MHz)
VMC	Visual meteorological conditions
VOLMET*	Meteorological information for aircraft in flight
VOR	VHF omnidirectional radio range
VORTAC*	VOR and TACAN combination

1.3   **HOURS OF SERVICE AND COMMUNICATIONS WATCH**

1.3.1   The hours of service of the radio facilities available in the United Kingdom are published in the UK AIP (COM 2) which also details those periods set aside for maintenance.

1.3.2   When an aircraft has established communication with an ATSU it is required to maintain a listening watch with that ATSU and advise the ATSU when the listening watch is about to cease. Aircraft will not cease to maintain a listening watch, except for reasons of safety, without informing the ATSU concerned. A time at which it is expected that the watch will be resumed must be stated.

1.4   **RECORD OF COMMUNICATIONS**

1.4.1   An aircraft telecommunication log-book is not required to be kept in respect of communication by radiotelephony with an aeronautical station which provides a radio service for aircraft. Many UK aeronautical stations have automatic recording equipment for air-ground communications but at those which do not a record is kept of all communications with aircraft.

1.5 CATEGORIES OF MESSAGE

1.5.1 The categories of messages handled by the aeronautical mobile service are in the following order of priority:

(a) Distress messages

(b) Urgency messages

} See Chapter 9

(c) Communications relating to direction finding

(d) Flight safety messages

(e) Meteorological messages

(f) Flight Regularity messages

CHAPTER 2-GENERAL OPERATING PROCEDURES

2.1   INTRODUCTION

2.1.1   Radiotelephony provides the means by which pilots and ground personnel communicate with each other. Used properly the information and instructions transmitted are of vital importance in assisting in the safe and expeditious operation of aircraft. However the use of non-standard procedures and phraseology can cause misunderstanding. Incidents and accidents have occurred in which a contributing factor has been the misunderstanding caused by the use of non-standard phraseology. The importance of using correct and precise standard phraseology cannot be over-emphasised.

2.2   TRANSMITTING TECHNIQUE

2.2.1   The following transmitting techniques will assist in ensuring that transmitted speech is clearly and satisfactorily received.

(a)   Before transmitting listen out on the frequency to be used to ensure that there will be no interference with a transmission from another station.

(b)   Be familiar with microphone operating techniques and do not turn your head away from it whilst talking or vary the distance between it and your mouth. Severe distortion of speech may arise from:

(i)   talking too close to the microphone

(ii)   touching the microphone with the lips

(iii)   holding the microphone or boom (of a combined headset/microphone system).

(c)   Use a normal conversational tone, speak clearly and distinctly.

(d)   Maintain an even rate of speech not exceeding 100 words per minute. When it is known that elements of the message will be written down by the recipients, speak at a slightly slower rate.

(e)   Maintain the speaking volume at a constant level.

(f)   A slight pause before and after numbers will assist in making them easier to understand.

(g)   Avoid using hesitation sounds such as 'er'.

(h)   Depress the transmit switch fully before speaking and do not release it until the message is complete. This will ensure that the entire message is transmitted. However, do not depress transmit switch until ready to speak.

(i)   Be aware that the mother tongue of the person receiving the message may not be English. Therefore, speak clearly and use standard radiotelephony (RTF) words and phrases wherever possible.

2.2.2   One of the most irritating and potentially dangerous situations in radiotelephony is a 'stuck' microphone button. Operators should always ensure that the button is released after a transmission and the microphone placed in an appropriate place that will ensure that it will not inadvertently be switched on.

2.3   TRANSMISSION OF LETTERS

2.3.1   The words in the table below shall be used when individual letters are required to be transmitted. The syllables to be emphasised are underlined.

Letter	Word	Appropriate pronunciation
A	Alpha	AL FAH
B	Bravo	BRAH VOH
C	Charlie	CHAR LEE
D	Delta	DELL TAH
E	Echo	ECK OH
F	Foxtrot	FOKS TROT
G	Golf	GOLF
H	Hotel	HOH TELL

Letter	Word	Appropriate pronunciation
I	India	<u>IN</u> DEE AH
J	Juliett	<u>JEW</u> LEE ETT
K	Kilo	<u>KEY</u> LOH
L	Lima	<u>LEE</u> MAH
M	Mike	MIKE
N	November	NO <u>VEM</u> BER
O	Oscar	<u>OSS</u> CAH
P	Papa	PAH <u>PAH</u>
Q	Quebec	KEH <u>BECK</u>
R	Romeo	<u>ROW</u> ME OH
S	Sierra	SEE <u>AIR</u> RAH
T	Tango	<u>TANG</u> GO
U	Uniform	<u>YOU</u> NEE FORM
V	Victor	<u>VIK</u> TAH
W	Whiskey	<u>WISS</u> KEY
X	X-ray	<u>ECKS</u> <u>RAY</u>
Y	Yankee	<u>YANG</u> KEE
Z	Zulu	<u>ZOO</u> LOO

2.4 TRANSMISSION OF NUMBERS

2.4.1 The syllables to be emphasised are underlined.

Numeral or numeral element	Latin alphabet representation
0	<u>ZERO</u>
1	<u>WUN</u>
2	<u>TOO</u>

Numeral or numeral element	Latin alphabet representation
3	TREE
4	FOWER
5	FIFE
6	SIX
7	SEVEN
8	AIT
9	NINER
Decimal	DAYSEEMAL
Thousand	TOUSAND

2.4.2   All numbers except whole thousands shall be transmitted by pronouncing each digit separately. Whole thousands shall be transmitted by pronouncing each digit in the number of thousands followed by the word thousand.

Number	Transmitted as	Pronounced as
10	One Zero	WUN ZERO
75	Seven Five	SEVEN FIFE
100	One Zero Zero	WUN ZERO ZERO
583	Five Eight Three	FIFE AIT TREE
2 500	Two Five Zero Zero	TOO FIFE ZERO ZERO
5 000	Five Thousand	FIFE TOUSAND
11 000	One One Thousand	WUN WUN TOUSAND
25 000	Two Five Thousand	TOO FIFE TOUSAND
38 143	Three Eight One Four Three	TREE AIT WUN FOWER TREE

2.4.3   Numbers containing a decimal point shall be transmitted as prescribed in 2.4.1 with the decimal point in appropriate sequence being indicated by the word decimal.

Number	Transmitted as	Pronounced as
118.1	One One Eight Decimal One	WUN WUN AIT DAY-SEE-MAL WUN
120.375	One Two Zero Decimal Three Seven	WUN TOO ZERO DAY-SEE-MAL TREE SEVEN

Note: Only the first five figures are used when identifying frequencies separated by 25 kHz.

2.4.4   When it is necessary to verify the accurate reception of numbers the person transmitting the message shall request the person receiving the message to read back the numbers.

2.5   **TRANSMISSION OF TIME**

2.5.1   When transmitting time, only the minutes of the hour are normally required. However, the hour should be included if there is any possibility of confusion. Time checks shall be given to the nearest minute. Co-ordinated Universal Time (UTC) is to be used at all times, unless specified. 2400 hours designates midnight, the end of the day, and 0000 hours the beginning of the day.

Time	Transmitted as	Pronounced as
0823	Two Three or Zero Eight Two Three	TOO TREE (or ZERO AIT TOO TREE)
1300	One Three Zero Zero	WUN TREE ZERO ZERO
2057	Five Seven or Two Zero Five Seven	FIFE SEVEN (or TOO ZERO FIFE SEVEN)

2.6   STANDARD WORDS AND PHRASES

2.6.1   The following words and phrases shall be used in radiotelephony communications as appropriate and shall have the meaning given below:

WORD/PHRASE	MEANING
ACKNOWLEDGE	Let me know that you have received and understood this message.
AFFIRM	Yes
APPROVED	Permission for proposed action granted.
BREAK	Indicates the separation between messages.
CANCEL	Annul the previously transmitted clearance.
CHECK	Examine a system or procedure (no answer is normally expected).
CLEARED	Authorised to proceed under the conditions specified.
CONFIRM	Have I correctly received the following...? or Did you correctly receive this message?
CONTACT	Establish radio contact with...
CORRECT	That is correct.
CORRECTION	An error has been made in this transmission (or message indicated). The correct version is...
DISREGARD	Consider that transmission as not sent.
HOW DO YOU READ	What is the readability of my transmission.

WORD/PHRASE	MEANING
I SAY AGAIN	I repeat for clarity or emphasis.
MONITOR	Listen out on (frequency).
NEGATIVE	No or Permission not granted or That is not correct.
OVER	My transmission is ended and I expect a response from you.
OUT	This exchange of transmissions is ended and no response is expected.
PASS YOUR MESSAGE	Proceed with your message.
READ BACK	Repeat all, or the specified part, of this message back to me exactly as received.
REPORT	Pass requested information.
REQUEST	I should like to know . . . or I wish to obtain . . .
ROGER	I have received all your last transmission. *Note: Under no circumstances to be used in reply to a question requiring a direct answer in the affirmative (AFFIRM) or negative (NEGATIVE).*
SAY AGAIN	Repeat all, or the following part of your last transmission.
SPEAK SLOWER	Reduce your rate of speech.
STANDBY	Wait and I will call you. *Note: No onward clearance to be assumed.*
VERIFY	Check and confirm.
WILCO	I understand your message and will comply with it (abbreviation for will comply)

2.7   COMMUNICATIONS

2.7.1   Callsigns for aeronautical stations

2.7.1.1   Aeronautical stations are identified by the name of the location followed by a suffix. The suffix indicates the type of service being provided.

Service	Suffix
area control service	CONTROL
radar (in general)	RADAR
approach control	APPROACH
aerodrome control	TOWER
ground movement control	GROUND
precision approach radar	PRECISION
flight information service	INFORMATION
aerodrome air/ground communications service	RADIO

2.7.1.2   There are three main categories of aeronautical communications service:

Air traffic control service (ATC) which can only be provided by licensed air traffic controllers;

Aerodrome flight information service (AFIS) which can be provided only by licensed aerodrome flight information service officers (AFISOs);

Aerodrome air/ground communications service (A/G) for which no air traffic service qualification is required. However, persons providing this service must possess an 'Authority to Operate'.

It is an offence to use a callsign for a purpose other than that for which it has been notified.

2.7.1.3   When satisfactory communication has been established, and provided that it will not be confusing, the name of the location or the callsign suffix may be omitted.

2.7.2   Aircraft Callsigns

2.7.2.1   When establishing communication an aircraft shall use the full callsigns of both stations.

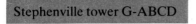

Stephenville tower G-ABCD	G-ABCD Stephenville tower

2.7.2.2   Pilots should confine their communications with a ground radio station to a range and height applicable to the service. At most international airports these figures are 25 nm and 4000 feet or less. Communication with ground stations outside these limits is technically possible but can result in interference to another service using the same frequency.

2.7.2.3   After satisfactory communication has been established and provided that no confusion is likely to occur, the ground station may abbreviate callsigns (see table below). A pilot may only abbreviate the callsign of his aircraft if it has first been abbreviated by the aeronautical ground station.

Type	Example	
	Full	Abbreviated
(a) the five-character callsign corresponding to the registration marking of the aircraft;	G-ABCD	G-CD
(b) the five-character callsign referred to in (a) above, preceded by the radiotelephony designator of the aircraft operating agency;	AIR CANADA CFCAD	AIR CANADA AD
(c) the five-character callsign referred to in (a) above, preceded by the type of the aircraft;	BEECHCRAFT G-ABCD	BEECHCRAFT CD
(d) the radiotelephony designator of the aircraft operating agency, followed by the flight identification;	SPEEDBIRD 725	no abbreviation permitted
(e) the characters corresponding to the registration marking of the aircraft.	N357826	N826

2.7.2.4　An aircraft shall not change its callsign type during a flight. However, where there is a likelihood that confusion may occur because of similar callsigns, an aircraft may be instructed by an air traffic service unit to change the type of its callsign temporarily.

2.7.2.5　Aircraft in the heavy wake turbulence category shall include the word 'HEAVY' immediately after the aircraft callsign in the initial call.

2.7.3　**Continuation of Communications**

2.7.3.1　After initial contact has been firmly established the following words may be omitted provided that no possibility of confusion or ambiguity will result:

(a)　the words 'over', 'roger' and 'out' may be omitted;

(b)　further identification or callsign may be omitted until termination of the communications.

2.7.3.2　When it is considered that reception is likely to be difficult, important elements of the message should be spoken twice.

2.7.3.3　When a ground station wishes to broadcast information to all aircraft likely to receive it, the message should be prefaced by the call 'All stations'.

> All stations Alexander control, Colinton VOR on test

No reply is expected to such general calls unless individual stations are subsequently called upon to acknowledge receipt.

2.7.3.4　If there is doubt that a message has been correctly received, a repetition of the message shall be requested either in full or in part.

Phrase	Meaning
Say again	Repeat entire message
Say again... (item)	
Say again all before... (the first word satisfactorily received)	
Say again all after... (the last word satisfactorily received)	Repeat specific item
Say again all between... and...	

2.7.3.5　When a station is called but is uncertain of the identification of the calling station, the calling station should be requested to repeat its callsign until identification is established.

Ground Fastair 345

Station calling Stephenville ground say again your call sign

2.7.3.6　When an error is made in a transmission the word 'CORRECTION' shall be spoken, the last correct group or phrase repeated and then the correct version transmitted.

Fastair 345 Wicken 47
FL 330 Marlow 07
correction Marlow 57

Fastair 345 roger

2.7.3.7　If a correction can best be made by repeating the entire message, the operator shall use the phrase 'CORRECTION I SAY AGAIN' before transmitting the message a second time.

2.7.4   Transfer of communications

2.7.4.1   An aircraft will normally be advised by the appropriate aeronautical station to change from one radio frequency to another in accordance with agreed procedures.

Fastair 345 contact
Alexander control 129.1

129.1 Fastair 345

In the absence of such advice, the aircraft shall notify the aeronautical station before such a change takes place. Aircraft flying in controlled airspace must obtain permission from the controlling authority before changing frequency.

2.7.4.2   An aircraft may be instructed to 'standby' on a frequency when it is intended that the ATSU will initiate further communications, and to monitor a frequency on which information is being broadcast.

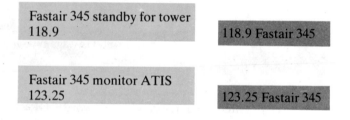

Fastair 345 standby for tower
118.9

118.9 Fastair 345

Fastair 345 monitor ATIS
123.25

123.25 Fastair 345

2.7.5   Issue of clearance and read back requirements

2.7.5.1   Provisions governing clearances are contained in the PANS-RAC (ICAO Doc 4444). A clearance may vary in content from a detailed description of the route and levels to be flown to a brief standard instrument departure (SID) according to local procedures.

2.7.5.2   Controllers will pass a clearance slowly and clearly since the pilot needs to write it down; wasteful repetition will thus be avoided. Whenever possible a route clearance should be passed to an aircraft before start up and the aircraft's full callsign will always be used. *Generally controllers will avoid passing a clearance to a pilot engaged in complicated taxying manoeuvres and on no occasion when the pilot is engaged in line up or take-off manoeuvres.*

2.7.5.3   An ATC route clearance is *not* an instruction to take-off or enter an active runway. *The words 'take-off' are used only when an aircraft is cleared for take-off. At all other times the word 'departure' is used.*

2.7.5.4   The stringency of the read back requirement is directly related to the possible seriousness of a misunderstanding in the transmission and receipt of ATC clearance and instructions. *ATC route clearances shall always be read back unless otherwise authorised by the appropriate ATS authority* in which case they shall be acknowledged in a positive manner. Read backs shall always include the aircraft callsign.

Fastair 345 cleared to Kennington, climb to and maintain FL 280, Wicken 1 november departure, squawk 5501

Fastair 345 is cleared to Kennington, maintain FL 280, Wicken 1 november departure, squawk 5501 Fastair 345

Fastair 345 correct

Fastair 345 cleared to Kennington, Wicken 3 delta departure, squawk 5501

Cleared to Kennington, Wicken 3 delta departure, squawk 5501 Fastair 345

Fastair 345 correct

G-CD after departure, right turn out, leave control zone via route echo

After departure, right turn out, leave control zone via route echo G-CD

G-CD correct

2.7.5.5　The following ATC messages listed below are to be read back in full by the pilot. If the controller does not receive a readback the pilot will be asked to do so. Similarly, the pilot is expected to request that instructions are repeated or clarified if any are not fully understood.

Level Instructions

Heading Instructions

Speed Instructions

Airways or Route Clearances

Clearance to Enter, Land On, Take-Off On, Backtrack or Cross an Active Runway

SSR Operating Instructions

Altimeter Settings

VDF Information

Frequency Changes

G-ABCD cleared to cross Amber 1 at Wicken FL 70	Cleared to cross Amber 1 at Wicken FL 70 G-ABCD
G-CD hold position	Holding G-CD
G-CD contact ground 118.05	118.05 G-CD
Fastair 345 Squawk 6402	Squawk 6402 Fastair 345

2.7.5.6　If an aircraft read back of a clearance or instruction is incorrect, the controller shall transmit the word 'NEGATIVE' followed by the correct version.

G-CD QNH 1003	QNH 1013 G-CD

Negative, QNH 1003

1003 G-CD

2.7.5.7   If at any time a pilot receives a clearance or instruction with which he cannot comply, he should advise the controller using the phrase 'UNABLE COMPLY' and give the reasons.

Fastair 345 Georgetown, cleared to Colinton FL 290, cross Wicken FL 150 or above	Georgetown Fastair 345 unable cross Wicken FL 150 due weight

2.7.6   Failure to establish or maintain communication

2.7.6.1   *Air to Ground*

(a)   Check the following points:

    (i)   The correct frequency has been selected for the route being flown.

    (ii)   The Aeronautical Station being called is open for watch.

    (iii)   The aircraft is not out of radio range.

(b)   If the previous points are in order it may be that the aircraft equipment is not functioning correctly. Complete the checks of headset and radio installation appropriate to the aircraft.

(c)   If the pilot is still unable to establish communication on any designated aeronautical station frequency, or with any other aircraft, the pilot is to transmit his message twice on the designated frequency preceded by the phrase 'TRANSMITTING BLIND' in case the transmitter is still functioning.

(d)   Where a transmitter failure is suspected, check or change the microphone. Listen out on the designated frequency for instructions. It should be possible to answer questions by use of the carrier wave if the microphone is not functioning.

(e) In the case of a receiver failure transmit reports twice at the scheduled times or positions on the designated frequency preceded by the phrase 'TRANSMITTING BLIND DUE TO RECEIVER FAILURE'.

(f) An aircraft which is being provided with air traffic control, advisory service or aerodrome flight information is to transmit information regarding the intention of the pilot in command with respect to the continuation of the flight. Specific procedures for the action to be taken by pilots of IFR and Special VFR flights are contained in the appropriate AIP (RAC) sections.

2.7.6.2 *Ground to Air*

After completing checks of ground equipment (most airports have standby and emergency communications equipment) the ground station will request other aeronautical stations and aircraft to attempt to communicate with the aircraft which has failed to maintain contact.

If still unable to establish communication the aeronautical station will transmit messages addressed to the aircraft by blind transmission on the frequency on which the aircraft is believed to be listening.

These will consist of:

(a) The level, route and EAT (or ETA) to which it is assumed the aircraft is adhering.

(b) The weather conditions at the destination aerodrome and suitable alternate and, if practicable, the weather conditions in an area or areas suitable for descent through cloud procedure to be effected. (See AIP RAC Section.)

2.7.7 **Test procedures**

2.7.7.1 Test transmissions should take the following form:

(a) the identification of the aeronautical station being called;

(b) the aircraft identification;   G B F L U

(c)   the words 'RADIO CHECK';

(d)   the frequency being used.

2.7.7.2   Replies to test transmissions should be as follows:

(a)   the identification of the station calling;

(b)   the identification of the station replying;

(c)   information regarding the readibility of the transmission.

2.7.7.3   The readability of a transmission should be classified by the number in the table below, together with any other information regarding the transmission which may be useful to the station making the test.

Scale	Meaning
1	Unreadable
2	Readable now and then
3	Readable but with difficulty
4	Readable
5	Perfectly readable

Stephenville tower
G-ABCD radio check 118.7

G-ABCD Stephenville tower
readability 5

or

G-CD Stephenville tower
readability 3 with a a loud
background whistle

or

Station calling Stephenville
tower readability 1

2.7.7.4   When it is necessary for a ground station to make test signals, either for the adjustment of a transmitter before making a call or for the adjustment of a receiver, such signals shall not continue for more than 10 seconds. The test should comprise spoken numbers (ONE, TWO, THREE etc) followed by the radio callsign of the station transmitting the test signals.

2.8   MILITARY AERODROME TRAFFIC ZONES AND ASSOCIATED PENETRATION SERVICES

2.8.1   Comprehensive details of MATZ and the associated penetration service, including controlling aerodromes, contact frequencies and hours of watch, are contained in the UK AIP RAC Section, AICs and NOTAM.

2.8.2   While every effort will be made to ensure safe separation, some civil aircraft flying within the MATZ may not be known to controllers and therefore pilots should keep a careful look-out at all times.

2.8.3   Pilots requiring a MATZ penetration service must establish two way RTF communication on the appropriate frequency with the aerodrome controlling the zone when 15 nm or 5 min flying time from the boundary whichever is the sooner.

Banksfield Approach G-ABCD request MATZ penetration	G-ABCD Banksfield Approach pass your details
	G-ABCD, Cessna 150 over Deenethorpe heading 350°, 1500 feet en-route Stephenville
	G-CD, cross MATZ at 1500 ft on QFE 1006. Report entering and leaving
	G-CD, cross at 1500 ft on QFE 1006, Wilco

Whilst working a MATZ unit, pilots are expected to comply with any instructions issued by controllers and maintain a listening watch on the allocated RTF frequency. They should not change heading or height without giving prior warning and should advise when clear of the MATZ.

2.9   LOWER AIRSPACE RADAR ADVISORY SERVICE

2.9.1   The Lower Airspace Radar Advisory Service (LARS) is available to assist pilots flying VFR or IFR in UK unregulated airspace. The service will be provided at the discretion of controllers and will commence when aircraft have been identified and pilots so informed.

2.9.2   Comprehensive details of LARS, including participating ATSUs, their hours of watch and contact frequencies, are contained in the UK AIP RAC Section, AICs and NOTAM.

2.9.3   While every effort will be made to ensure safe separation, some aircraft may not be known to controllers and pilots should keep a very careful look-out at all times.

2.9.4   Pilots requiring a LARS must establish two way RTF communication on the appropriate frequency with the nearest participating ATSU.

> Banksfield Approach
> G-BJCD request Lower
> Airspace Radar Service

> G-BJCD Banksfield
> Approach pass your details

> G-BJCD C150 30 miles
> SW Banksfield heading 025°
> 3000 feet, destination
> Bakerley

2.10   PILOTS COMPLAINTS CONCERNING AERONAUTICAL TELECOMMUNICATIONS

Pilots' reports of faults concerning services and facilities in the Aeronautical Mobile, Broadcast and Navigation Services may be recorded on the CAA Form CA 647. The Pilot should ensure that the Briefing Officer, Senior Telecommunications Officer or Senior Controller at the destination or airport of first landing receives full details in order that remedial action can be taken. Reports of local unserviceabilities will be forwarded to the Telecommunications staff if received on RTF by the ATSU.

2.11 AIR TRAFFIC SERVICE COMPLAINTS ABOUT AIRCRAFT COMMUNICATIONS

Aircraft radio faults including technical failure, incorrect operating procedures and misuse of specific radio channels may result in the aircraft operator receiving a CAA Form CA 163 which details the fault condition and invites the operator to explain and/or state what corrective action has been taken.

CHAPTER 3–GENERAL PHRASEOLOGY

3.1   INTRODUCTION

3.1.1   The phraseology detailed in this manual has been established for the purpose of ensuring uniformity in RTF communications. Obviously, it is not practicable to detail phraseology examples suitable for every situation which may occur. However, if standard phrases are adhered to when composing a message, any possible ambiguity will be reduced to a minimum.

3.1.2   Some abbreviations, which by their common usage have become part of aviation terminology, may be spoken using their constituent letters rather than the spelling alphabet, for example, ILS, QNH, RVR, etc, (see para 1.2).

3.1.3   The following words may be omitted from transmissions provided that no confusion or ambiguity will result:

(a)   'Surface' and 'knots' in relation to surface wind direction and speed.

(b)   'Degrees' in relation to surface wind direction and headings.

(c)   'Visibility', 'cloud' and 'height' in meteorological reports.

(d)   'Millibars' when giving pressure settings.

Note: The 'millibar' will be replaced by the 'hectopascal' after 31 December 1985.

3.1.4   The use of excessive courtesies should be avoided.

3.2   LEVEL INSTRUCTIONS

3.2.1   Only basic level instructions are detailed in this chapter. More comprehensive phrases are contained in subsequent chapters in the context in which they are most commonly used.

3.2.2   The precise phraseology used in the transmission and acknowledgement of climb and descent clearances will vary, depending upon the circumstances, traffic density and nature of the flight operations.

3.2.3   However, care must be taken to ensure that misunderstandings are not generated as a consequence of the phraseology employed during these phases of flight. For example, levels may be reported as altitude, height or flight levels according to the phase of flight and the altimeter setting.

3.2.3.1 In the following examples the operations of climbing and descending are interchangeable and examples of only one form are given.

G-CD report your level	G-CD maintaining 3 000 feet QNH 1014
G-CD report passing FL 80	G-CD wilco
	G-CD passing FL 80
G-CD maintain 2 500 feet	G-CD maintaining 2 500 feet
G-CD climb FL 70	G-CD leaving 2 000 feet for FL 70
G-CD request descent	G-CD descend FL 60
	G-CD leaving FL 90 for FL 60
Fastair 345 after passing North Cross descend FL 80	Fastair 345 after North Cross descend FL 80

Fastair 345 stop descent at FL 150	
	Stop descent at FL 150 Fastair 345

3.2.3.2 *Occasionally*, for traffic reasons, a higher than normal rate of climb or descent may be required.

Fastair 345 expedite descent to FL 80	Fastair 345 expediting descent to FL 80
Fastair 345 climb to FL 240 expedite until passing FL 180	Fastair 345 climbing to FL 240 expediting until passing FL 180

or

Fastair 345 unable expedite climb

3.3   POSITION REPORTING

3.3.1   Position reports shall contain the following elements of information:

(1)   Aircraft identification

(2)   Position

(3)   Time

(4)   Level

(5)   Next position and ETA

Fastair 345 Wicken 47 FL 330 Marlow 57	Fastair 345 roger

31

3.3.2   Where adequate flight progress data is available from other sources, such as ground radar, aircraft may be exempted from the requirement to make compulsory position reports.

Fastair 345 next report at Colinton	Fastair 345 wilco
Fastair 345 omit position reports this frequency	Fastair 345 wilco
Fastair 345 resume position reporting	Fastair 345 wilco

3.4   FLIGHT PLANS

3.4.1   A pilot may file a flight plan with an ATSU during flight, although the use of busy RTF channels should be avoided. Details should be passed using the flight plan format.

Alexander control G-ABCD request file flight plan	G-ABCD Alexander control roger ready to copy

3.4.2   During a flight a pilot may elect to cancel an IFR flight plan.

Alexander control G-CD cancel my IFR flight plan	G-CD roger IFR flight plan cancelled at time 47

3.4.3   When a pilot has expressed his intention to cancel an IFR flight plan, the ATSU will pass the pilot any available meteorological information which makes it likely that flight in VMC cannot be maintained.

G-CD IMC reported in the vicinity of Kennington	G-CD roger maintaining IFR

32

CHAPTER 4 – AERODROME AIR TRAFFIC SERVICES: AIRCRAFT

4.1 INTRODUCTION

4.1.1 Concise and unambiguous phraseology used at the correct time is vital to the smooth, safe and expeditious running of an aerodrome. It is not only the means by which instructions and information are passed but it also assists pilots in maintaining an awareness of other traffic in their vicinity, particularly in poor visibility conditions.

4.1.2 Messages will not be transmitted to an aircraft during take-off, the last part of final approach or the landing roll, unless it is necessary for safety reasons, because it will be distracting to the pilot at a time when the cockpit workload is often at its highest.

4.1.3 Local procedures vary from aerodrome to aerodrome and it is impossible to give examples to cover every situation which may arise at the multiplicity of different types of aerodrome. Information in addition to that shown in the examples, eg. time checks, etc. may be provided as necessary.

4.2 TYPE OF SERVICE

4.2.1 As described in Chapter 2 the type of service provided at an aerodrome falls into one of three categories. In this chapter the examples are confined to those used by air traffic controllers and aerodrome flight information service officers.

4.2.2 It should be noted that the phraseology used by AFISOs for take-off and landing is different from that used by controllers. Other phraseology is the same but an AFISO, on his own initiative, will give only that which relates to flight information. Therefore, pilots must ensure that they maintain their own separation from other aircraft and cannot expect either instructions or advice on any course of action.

4.2.3   AFISOs are, however, permitted to pass messages on behalf of other agencies. If they do so, they will include the name of the agency so that pilots will be aware that the message comes from a legitimate source. eg. 'London control clears you to join.....'

4.3   **DEPARTURE INFORMATION AND ENGINE STARTING PROCEDURES**

4.3.1   Where no ATIS is provided the pilot may ask for current aerodrome information before requesting start up.

> Stephenville ground
> Fastair 345 IFR to Colinton, request departure information

> Fastair 345 departure runway 32 wind 290 degrees 4 knots, QNH 1022, temperature –2, dewpoint –3, RVR 550 metres

> Runway 32, QNH 1022, will call you for start up Fastair 345

4.3.2   Requests to start engines are normally made to facilitate ATC planning and to avoid excessive fuel wastage by aircraft delayed on the ground. At certain aerodromes, along with the request, the pilot will state the location of the aircraft and acknowledge receipt of the ATIS broadcast identifying letter.

> Georgetown Ground
> Fastair 345, stand 24 information bravo, request start up

> Fastair 345 start up at time 35

4.3.3   When there will be a delay to the departure of the aircraft the controller will normally indicate a time to start up or expect to start up.

Stephenville ground Fastair 345 request start up	Fastair 345 start up approved
	or
	Fastair expect start up at time 35
	or
	Fastair 345 expect departure at time 49 start up at your discretion

4.4 PUSHBACK

4.4.1 At many aerodromes at which large aircraft operate, the aircraft are parked nose-in to the terminal in order to save parking space. Aircraft have to be pushed backwards by tugs before they can taxi for departure. Requests for pushback are made to ATC depending on the local procedures.

Ground Fastair 345 stand 27 request pushback	Fastair 345 pushback approved
	or
	Fastair 345 negative. Expect one minute delay due B747 taxying behind

4.5 TAXI INSTRUCTIONS

4.5.1 Taxi instructions issued by a controller will always contain a clearance limit, which is the point at which the aircraft must stop unless further permission to proceed is given. For departing aircraft the clearance limit will normally be the holding point of the runway in use, but it may be any other position on the aerodrome depending on the prevailing traffic.

Stephenville tower G-ABCD C172 by the south side hangars request taxi for VFR local flight	G-CD taxi to holding point runway 24 via taxiway charlie wind 250 8 QNH 1010

G-CD QNH 1010 request
runway 14

G-CD taxi to holding point
runway 14, follow the Seneca
coming from your left

G-CD holding point
runway 14 traffic in sight

Stephenville tower G-ABCD
C172 at the fuel station
VFR to Walden request taxi

G-CD runway 06 wind
080 degrees 10 knots
QNH 1012 taxi via taxiway
alpha to holding point
runway 14

QNH 1012 request taxiway
bravo, and backtrack G-CD

G-CD approved taxi via
bravo, backtrack and line up
runway 06

Stephenville tower G-ABCD
at the fuel station request
taxi to flying club

G-CD taxi to holding point
runway 24 via charlie

G-CD holding point 24
via charlie

G-CD approaching holding
point request cross
runway 24

G-CD negative hold short
runway 24

G-CD holding

G-CD cross runway 24 at the
threshold report vacated

G-CD cross runway 24 at the
threshold

G-CD runway vacated

G-CD taxi to flying club

G-CD

4.5.2 Where the ATIS broadcast is established the controller does not
need to pass departure information to the pilot when giving taxi
instructions.

Georgetown ground
Fastair 345 information
bravo request taxi

Fastair 345 after the B747
passing left to right taxi
to holding point runway 24

Taxi to holding point runway
24, traffic in sight Fastair 345

4.6   PRE-DEPARTURE MANOEUVRING

4.6.1   Meticulous care has been taken to ensure that the phraseology which is to be employed during the pre-departure manoeuvres cannot be interpreted as a take-off clearance. This is to avoid the serious consequences that could result if there is any mis-understanding in the granting or acknowledgement of take-off clearances.

4.6.2   At busy aerodromes with a separate ground and tower function, aircraft are usually transferred to the tower frequency at or approaching the holding point.

Fastair 345 contact tower 118.9	118.9 Fastair 345

4.6.3   Many types of aircraft carry out engine checks prior to departure and are not always ready for take-off when they reach the holding point.

G-CD report when ready for departure	G-CD wilco
G-CD ready for departure	G-CD line up
	G-CD lining up

4.7   TAKE-OFF PROCEDURES

4.7.1   Except in cases of emergency, messages will not be transmitted to an aircraft in the process of taking off or in the final stages of an approach and landing.

Controllers will use the following phraseology for take off.

G-CD cleared take-off	Cleared take-off G-CD

AFISOs will use different phraseology to indicate that there is nothing to prevent an aircraft taking off:

> Walden Information
> G-BJCD is ready for
> departure

> G-CD Walden Information
> take-off at your discretion..
> .....(traffic information)

4.7.2   For traffic reasons a controller may consider it necessary for an aircraft to take-off immediately after lining up.

> Fastair 345 are you ready
> for immediate departure

> Fastair 345 affirm

> Fastair 345 line up be ready
> for immediate departure

> Fastair 345 lining up

> Fastair 345 cleared
> immediate take-off

> Cleared immediate take-off
> Fastair 345

4.7.3   In poor visibility the controller may request the pilot to report when airborne.

Fastair cleared take-off report airborne	Cleared take-off Fastair 345 wilco

	Fastair 345 airborne 57

	Fastair 345 contact radar 121.75

	121.75 Fastair 345

4.7.4 Conditional phrases will not be used for movements affecting the active runway(s), except when the aircraft or vehicles concerned are seen by the controller and pilot. When the conditional clearance involves a departing aircraft and an arriving aircraft it is important to ensure that the departing aircraft has correctly identified the arriving aircraft on which the conditional clearance is based. Reference to the arriving aircraft type may be insufficient and a controller may give further information to be passed to ensure correct identification. A conditional instruction shall be given as follows:

(a)   callsign;

(b)   the condition;

(c)   the instruction.

Fastair 345 report the DC9 on final in sight	Fastair 345 DC9 in sight

	Fastair 345 after that DC9 line up

	After the DC9 line up Fastair 345

4.7.5   When several runways are in use and there is any possibility that the pilot may be confused as to which one to use, the runway number will be stated.

> Fastair 345 cleared take-off runway 09

> Cleared take-off runway 09 Fastair 345

4.7.6   Local departure instructions may be given with the take-off clearance. Such instructions are normally given to ensure separation between aircraft operating in the vicinity of the aerodrome.

> Fastair 345 climb straight ahead until passing 2 500 feet before turning right cleared take-off

> Roger, straight ahead until 2 500 feet before turning right Fastair 345

> G-CD request right turn when airborne

> G-CD right turn approved cleared take-off

4.7.7   Due to unexpected traffic developments or a departing aircraft taking longer to take-off than anticipated, it is occasionally necessary to rescind the take-off clearance or quickly free the runway for landing traffic.

> Fastair 345 take-off immediately or vacate runway

> Fastair 345 taking off

> Fastair 345 take-off immediately or hold short of runway

> Fastair 345 holding short

41

4.7.8   When an aircraft is about to take-off or has commenced the take-off
         roll, and it is necessary that the aircraft should abandon take-off,
         the aircraft will be instructed to stop immediately and this
         instruction will be repeated.

G-CD hold position,
cancel I say again cancel
take-off, acknowledge

G-CD holding

Fastair 345 stop immediately
I say again Fastair 345 stop
immediately, acknowledge

Fastair 345 stopping

4.7.9   When a pilot abandons take-off he should, as soon as practicable,
         inform the tower that he is doing so. Likewise, as soon as
         practicable, he should inform the tower of the reasons for
         abandoning take-off if applicable, and request further manoeuvring
         instructions.

Fastair 345 stopping

Fastair 345

Fastair 345 request backtrack
for another departure

Fastair 345 backtrack
approved

42

4.8   AERODROME TRAFFIC CIRCUIT

4.8.1

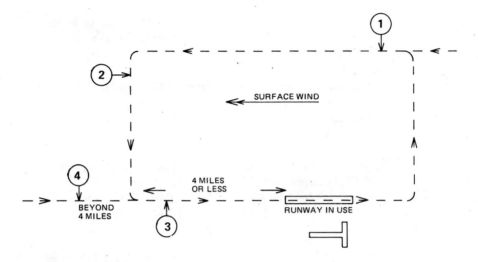

Typical Left-hand Circuit

Position 1   Aircraft reports on downwind leg when abeam upwind end of the runway.

Position 2   Base leg report (if required).

Position 3   'Final' report. Clearance to land issued here.

Position 4   'Long final' report (between 8 and 4 miles) when aircraft is on a straight in approach.

Fig 1   Critical position in the traffic circuit

4.8.2   Requests for circuit-joining instructions should be made in sufficient time for a planned entry into the circuit taking other traffic into account. Where ATIS is established, receipt of the broadcast should be acknowledged in the initial call to an aerodrome. When the traffic circuit is a right-hand pattern it shall be specified. A left-hand pattern need not be specified although it is essential to do so when the circuit direction is variable.

Walden tower G-ABCD C172 10 miles north 2 500 feet for landing	G-CD join righthand downwind runway 24 QFE 1006
	G-CD righthand downwind runway 24 QFE 1006

4.8.3   Depending on prevailing traffic conditions and the direction from which an aircraft is arriving, it may be possible to make a straight-in approach.

Walden tower G-ABCD C172 10 miles north 2 500 feet for landing	G-CD cleared straight in approach runway 17 wind 190 degrees 5 knots QFE 1006
	Cleared straight in approach runway 17 QFE 1006 G-CD

4.8.4   The pilot having joined the traffic circuit makes routine reports as required by local procedures.

G-CD downwind	G-CD number 2 follow the Cherokee on base
	G-CD number 2, traffic in sight
G-CD base	G-CD report final
G-CD final	G-CD continue approach wind 270 degrees 7 knots

4.8.5   It may be necessary in order to co-ordinate traffic in the circuit to issue delaying or expediting instructions.

> G-CD extend downwind number 2 to a Cherokee 4 miles final

> G-CD wilco

> G-CD make one orbit right report again on final traffic on runway

> G-CD wilco

4.9   FINAL APPROACH AND LANDING

4.9.1   A 'final' report is made when an aircraft turns onto final approach. If the turn on is made at a distance greater than 4 nm from touchdown a 'long final' report is made.

> G-CD final

> G-CD cleared to land wind 270 degrees 7 knots

> Cleared to land G-CD

> Fastair 345 long final

> Fastair 345 report final wind 260 18

> Fastair 345 final

> Fastair 345 cleared to land wind 270 20

> Cleared to land Fastair 345

Note: Where established an 'outer marker' instead of a 'final' report may be made.

4.9.2   A landing aircraft may be permitted to touch down before a preceding landing aircraft which has landed is clear of the runway provided that:

(a)   the runway is long enough to allow safe separation between the two aircraft and there is no evidence to indicate that braking may be adversely affected;

(b)   it is during daylight hours;

(c)   the controller is satisfied that the landing aircraft will be able to see the preceding aircraft which has landed, clearly and continuously, until it is clear of the runway; and

(d)   the pilot of the following aircraft is warned. (Responsibility for ensuring adequate separation rests with the pilot of the following aircraft.)

Fastair 345, land after the B737	Land after the B737 Fastair 345

4.9.3   A pilot may request to fly past the control tower or other observation point for the purpose of visual inspection from the ground.

Fastair 345 request low pass unsafe left gear indication	Fastair 345 cleared low pass not below 500 feet QFE 1006 report final
	Not below 500 feet QFE 1006 Fastair 345

4.9.4   If the low pass is made for the purpose of observing the under-
         carriage, one of the following replies could be used to describe its
         condition but these examples are not exhaustive:

(a)   landing gear appears down;

(b)   right (or left, or nose) wheel appears up (or down);

(c)   wheels appear up;

(d)   right (or left, or nose) wheel does not appear up (or down).

4.9.5   For training purposes, a pilot may request permission to make an
         approach along, or parallel to the runway, without landing.

Fastair 345 request low approach	Fastair 345 cleared low approach not below 250 feet report final
	Not below 250 feet Fastair 345

4.9.6   In order to save taxying time when flying training in the traffic
         circuit pilots may request to carry out a 'touch and go', ie. the
         aircraft lands, continues rolling and takes-off, without stopping.

G-CD request touch and go	G-CD cleared touch and go
	Cleared touch and go G-CD
	or
	G-CD unable to approve due traffic make full stop landing cleared to land
	Cleared to land for a full stop G-CD

4.9.7   AFISOs will use different phraseology to indicate that there is nothing to prevent an aircraft from landing or, alternatively, that the runway is obstructed.

> Walden Information G-BJCD final runway 24

> G-CD Walden Information, land at your discretion surface wind 260 degrees 6 knots QFE 1006

or

> G-CD Walden Information the runway is obstructed

4.10   GO AROUND

4.10.1   Instructions to carry out a missed approach may be given to avert an unsafe situation. When a missed approach is initiated cockpit workload is inevitably high. Any transmissions to aircraft going around will be brief and kept to a minimum.

> Fastair 345 go around I say again go around acknowledge

> Fastair 345 going around

4.10.2   In the event of a missed approach unless instructions are issued to the contrary, an aircraft on an instrument approach is to carry out the published missed approach procedure and an aircraft operating VFR is to continue into the normal traffic circuit.

4.10.3   In the event of missed approach being initiated by the pilot the phrase 'going around' shall be used.

> G-CD going around

> G-CD roger

4.11   **AFTER LANDING**

4.11.1   Unless absolutely necessary, controllers will not give taxi instructions to pilots until the landing roll is complete. Unless otherwise advised pilots should remain on tower frequency until the runway is vacated.

Fastair 345 vacate left	Vacate left Fastair 345
Fastair 345 take next right when vacated contact ground 118.35	Next right 118.35 Fastair 345
	Georgetown ground Fastair 345 runway vacated
	Fastair 345 taxi to stand 27 via taxiway alpha
	Fastair 345
G-CD taxi to the end report runway vacated	G-CD runway vacated
	G-CD taxi to the flying club

4.12   **ESSENTIAL AERODROME INFORMATION**

4.12.1   Essential aerodrome information is information regarding the manoeuvring area and its associated facilities which is necessary to ensure the safe operation of aircraft. Aerodrome information is passed to aircraft whenever possible prior to start-up or taxi and prior to the commencement of final approach.

> Fastair 345 caution construction work at the end of stand 37

> ...caution work in progress ahead north side of taxiway alpha

> ...caution centre line taxiway lighting unserviceable

> ...caution VASIS runway 27 unserviceable

> ...caution large flock of birds north of runway 27 near central taxiway

CHAPTER 5–AERODROME AIR TRAFFIC SERVICES: VEHICLES

5.1 INTRODUCTION

5.1.1 The expeditious movement of vehicles plays an essential supporting role in the operation of an aerodrome. Whenever possible the areas in which vehicles and aircraft operate are segregated. However, there are many occasions when vehicles need to move on the manoeuvring area either for maintenance purposes or in direct support of aircraft operations.

5.1.2 Procedures governing the movement of vehicles vary widely from aerodrome to aerodrome but certain factors to be taken into account when driving on an aerodrome are common to all:

(a) in general, aircraft are by no means as manoeuvrable as ground vehicles;

(b) the visibility from an aircraft cockpit for ground movement purposes is often restricted as compared with a vehicle.

Therefore when vehicles are operating in close proximity to aircraft, drivers should be extremely vigilant and comply with Rule 33 of the Rules of the Air and ATC Regulations 1981 and, if applicable, ATC instructions.

5.1.3 Correct RTF operating technique must be observed by all users. For all vehicles on the movement area, it is important that a continuous listening watch is maintained, not only in case of further instructions or information from the tower, but also so that drivers can be aware of the movements, and intended movements, of other traffic thereby reducing the risk of confliction.

5.2 MOVEMENT INSTRUCTIONS

5.2.1 Drivers on first call should identify themselves by their vehicle call sign, state their position and intended destination (and possibly required route).

> Ground Works 21 stand 27 request proceed to work in progress taxiway hotel

> Works 21 proceed to taxiway hotel via kilo and alpha

5.2.2   If the controller is too busy he will reply 'standby'. This means that the driver should wait until the controller calls back. The driver shall *not* proceed until permission is given.

5.2.3   When there is conflicting traffic the controller may reply 'hold position'. This means that the driver shall not proceed until the controller calls back with permission. All other replies should contain a clearly defined point to which the driver may proceed; this may or may not be the intended destination. If it is not the intended destination drivers must stop at this point and further permission shall be requested.

> Ground Tels 5 exit kilo request proceed to hangar 3

> Tels 5 proceed via kilo, alpha and foxtrot, cross runway 09. Hold short of runway 14

> Tels 5 proceeding via kilo, alpha and foxtrot to cross runway 09 hold short runway 14

5.2.4   Permission to proceed on the apron may include instructions to ensure safe operations.

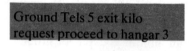

> Ground Tug 5 gate 21 request proceed to gate 26

> Tug 5 give way to the Fastair B737 on your right, then proceed to gate 26, caution jet blast

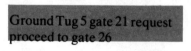

> Tug 5 giving way to the B737.

Caution: Drivers should be aware that if the phrase 'GO AHEAD' is used this is *NOT* an indication to proceed but only an invitation to pass a message. This phrase may be used by some controllers instead of 'PASS YOUR MESSAGE'.

5.3 CROSSING RUNWAYS

5.3.1 Drivers should note carefully the position to which they may proceed, particularly where the intended route involves crossing a runway. Some aerodromes may have procedures that will allow vehicles to proceed to a holding point on the movement area and then request runway crossing instructions. Under no circumstances shall a driver cross a runway unless *positive permission has been given and acknowledged.* A runway vacated report should not be made until the vehicle (and tow) is clear of the designated runway area.

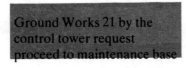

Ground Works 21 by the control tower request proceed to maintenance base

Works 21 proceed via india and bravo, hold short of runway 27

Works 21 hold short of runway 27

Works 21 holding short runway 27

Works 21 hold position

Works 21 holding

Works 21 cross runway 27 at threshold report vacated

Works 21 cross runway 27 at the threshold

> Works 21 runway 27 vacated

> Works 21 proceed via North
> taxiway to maintenance area

5.3.2   If a vehicle is operating on the runway, it will be called to leave the runway when it is expected that an aircraft will be landing or taking off.

> Works 21 vacate runway 27
> take next right, report
> vacated

> Works 21 wilco

> Works 21 runway 27 vacated

> Works 21 tower roger.

5.3.3   When a vehicle is moving on the movement area it may be necessary to inform the vehicle of a potentially dangerous situation and to tell it to stop.

> Works 21 stop immediately
> aircraft crossing ahead

> Works 21 stopping

5.4   VEHICLES TOWING AIRCRAFT

5.4.1   Drivers of vehicles required to tow aircraft should not assume that the receiving station is aware that an aircraft is to be towed. The performance and manoeuvrability of ground vehicles is obviously considerably reduced when towing aircraft and this is taken into account when instructions to such vehicles are issued. Therefore, in order to avoid any confusion, and as an aid to identification, drivers should state the type, and where applicable the operator, of the aircraft to be towed.

Ground tug 9 request tow Fastair B737 from stand 25 to maintenance hangar 3

Tug 9, tow approved from stand 25 via west taxiway to maintenance hangar 3

Ground tug 9 request tow Fastair B737 from maintenance hangar 3 to stand 25

Tug 9 proceed via holding point foxtrot, hold short runway 32

Tug 9 hold short runway 32

CHAPTER 6 – GENERAL RADAR PHRASEOLOGY

6.1 INTRODUCTION

6.1.1   This chapter contains general radar phraseology which is commonly used in communications between aircraft and all types of radar unit. Phraseology which is more applicable to approach radar control or area control is to be found in Chapter 7 and 8 as appropriate.

6.1.2   The phrase 'under radar control' shall only be used when a radar control service is being provided. Normally however, the callsign suffix used by the radar unit is sufficient to indicate its function.

6.1.3   In a radar environment heading information given by the pilot and heading instructions given by controllers are normally in degrees magnetic.

6.2 RADAR IDENTIFICATION AND VECTORING

6.2.1   An aircraft must be identified before it can be provided with a radar control or advisory service. However, the act of identifying aircraft is not a service in itself and pilots should not assume that they are receiving a radar service; particularly when they are flying outside controlled airspace.

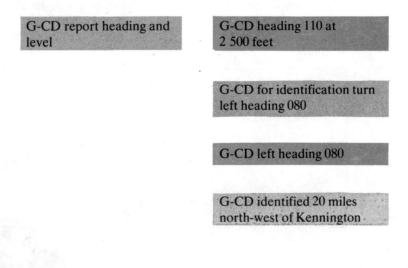

G-CD report heading and level

G-CD heading 110 at 2 500 feet

G-CD for identification turn left heading 080

G-CD left heading 080

G-CD identified 20 miles north-west of Kennington

G-CD

or

G-CD not identified. Resume own navigation

G-CD wilco

6.2.2   The pilot will be warned if identification is lost, or about to be lost, and appropriate instructions given.

G-CD identification lost due radar failure. Resume own navigation and contact Alexander Control on 128.75	128.75 G-CD

G-CD I will shortly lose identification. Contact Alexander Control on 128.75	128.75 G-CD

6.3   SECONDARY SURVEILLANCE RADAR

6.3.1   The following phrases are instructions which may be given by controllers to pilots regarding the operation of SSR transponders. The phrases used by controllers are given together with their meanings.

Phrase	Meaning
Squawk (code)	Set the mode and code as instructed
Confirm squawk	Confirm the mode and code set on the transponder
Recycle (mode) (code)	Reselect assigned mode and code

Phrase	Meaning
Squawk ident	Operate the special position identification feature
Squawk low	Select 'low sensitivity' feature
Squawk normal	Select normal feature
Squawk standby	Select the standby feature
Squawk charlie	Select altitude reporting feature
Check altimeter setting and confirm level	Check pressure setting and confirm your level
Stop squawk charlie	Deselect altitude feature
*Verify level	Check and confirm your level

*Used to verify the accuracy of the Mode C derived level information displayed to the controller.

6.3.2   The pilot must respond to SSR instructions, reading back specific settings.

Fastair 345 squawk 6411	6411 Fastair 345
Fastair 345 confirm squawk	6411 Fastair 345
Fastair 345 recycle 6411	Recycling 6411 Fastair 345
Fastair 345 check altimeter and confirm setting	Altimeter checked setting 1013, Fastair 345
Fastair 345 confirm transponder operating	Fastair 345 negative, transponder unserviceable.

59

6.4   RADAR CONTROL

6.4.1   Where it is not self-evident pilots will normally be informed by the controller when they are under radar control.

Fastair 345 under radar control	Fastair 345
	Fastair 345 radar control terminated
	Fastair 345

6.5   RADAR VECTORING

6.5.1   Aircraft may be given specific vectors to fly in order to establish separation. Pilots may be informed of the reasons for radar vectoring.

Fastair 345 for positioning turn left heading 050	Left heading 050 Fastair 345

6.5.2   It may be necessary for a controller to know the heading of an aircraft as separation can often be established by instructing an aircraft to continue on its existing heading.

Fastair 345 continue present heading	Fastair 345 wilco
Fastair 345 report heading	Fastair 345 heading 050
	Fastair 345 roger continue heading 050

Fastair 345 heading 050

6.5.3   When vectoring is complete, pilots will be instructed to resume their own navigation, given position information and appropriate instructions as necessary.

Fastair 345 resume own navigation direct Wicken magnetic track 070 distance 27 miles

Fastair 345 wilco

G-CD resume own navigation position 15 miles southwest of Kennington

G-CD wilco

6.5.4   Occasionally an aircraft may be instructed to make a complete turn (known as an orbit or a 360 degree turn), for delaying purposes or to achieve a required spacing behind preceding traffic.

G-CD make one orbit left for sequencing

One orbit left G-CD

Fastair 345 for delaying action make a three sixty turn left

Three sixty turn left Fastair 345

6.6   TRAFFIC INFORMATION AND AVOIDING ACTION

6.6.1   Whenever practicable, information regarding traffic on a conflicting path should be given in the following form:

(a)   relative bearing of the conflicting traffic in terms of the 12 hour clock;

(b)   distance from the conflicting traffic;

(c)   direction of flight of the conflicting traffic; and

(d)   relative speed of the conflicting traffic or the type of aircraft and level if this is known.

6.6.2   Relative movement should be described by using one of the following terms as applicable:

'closing, converging, parallel, same direction, opposite direction diverging, overtaking, crossing left to right, crossing right to left.'

6.6.3   Depending on the circumstances, vectors may be offered by the controller or requested by the pilot. The controller will inform the pilot when the conflict no longer exists.

Fastair 345 unknown traffic 10 o'clock 5 miles crossing left to right fast moving

Fastair 345 traffic not seen, request vectors

Fastair 345 turn left heading 050

Left heading 050 Fastair 345

Fastair 345 clear of traffic resume own navigation direct Wicken magnetic track 070 distance 27 miles

Fastair 345 proceeding direct Wicken

G-CD traffic 2 o'clock
5 miles north bound Cherokee
at 2 500 feet

G-CD

G-CD do you want vectors

G-CD negative vectors,
traffic in sight

G-CD clear of traffic

G-CD

6.6.4   Avoiding action to be taken by the pilot is given when the controller
considers that an imminent risk of collision will exist if action is not
taken immediately.

Fastair 345 avoiding action
turn left immediately
heading 110

Left heading 110
Fastair 345

Fastair 345 unknown traffic
2 o'clock 3 miles crossing
right to left fast moving

Fastair 345

6.7   **RADAR ASSISTANCE TO AIRCRAFT WITH
RADIOCOMMUNICATIONS FAILURE**

6.7.1   When a controller suspects that an aircraft is able to receive but not
transmit messages, the radar may be used to confirm that the pilot
has received instructions. When further instructions are given they
should be passed slowly, clearly and be repeated.

G-CD reply not received if
you read turn left
heading 040 I say again
turn left heading 040

G-CD turn observed I will
continue to pass instructions

or

Fastair 345 reply not
received if you read squawk
ident I say again squawk ident

Fastair 345 squawk observed
I will continue to pass
instructions

*Note: An aircraft experiencing a radiocommunications failure is
expected to select the appropriate SSR code.*

CHAPTER 7 – APPROACH CONTROL

7.1   IFR DEPARTURES

7.1.1   At many airports both arrivals and departures are handled by a single approach control unit. At busier airports departures and arrivals may be handled separately.

7.1.2   In addition to the ATC route clearance, departing IFR flights may be given additional instructions to provide separation in the immediate vicinity.

> Georgetown approach
> Fastair 345

> Fastair 345 continue heading 040 until passing FL 70 then direct Wicken

> Heading 040 until passing FL 70 Fastair 345

> Fastair 345 report passing FL 70

> Fastair 345 passing FL 70 routeing direct Wicken

> Fastair 345 contact Alexander Control 129.1

> Alexander Control 129.1 Fastair 345

7.2   VFR DEPARTURES

7.2.1   Departing VFR flights, when handled by approach control, may be passed information on relevant known traffic in order to assist the pilot in maintaining his own separation. Pilots should report leaving the area of jurisdiction of the approach control units.

Approach G-CD passing the zone boundary	G-CD flight information available from Alexander information 125.75
	125.75 G-CD

7.2.2   Special VFR flights will be cleared to leave the control zone in accordance with laid down procedures.

G-CD is cleared to the zone boundary via route Whiskey special VFR not above 1500 feet	G-CD is cleared to the zone boundary via route Whiskey special VFR not above 1500 feet
	G-CD correct

7.3   IFR ARRIVALS

7.3.1   Aircraft flying within controlled airspace will normally receive descent clearance to the clearance limit from the ATCC prior to transfer to an approach control unit. On transfer to approach control further descent instructions may be given.

Georgetown approach Fastair 345 descending to FL 80 estimating North Cross 46	Fastair 345 cleared for NDB approach descend FL 60 report beacon outbound

> Fastair 345 leaving FL 80
> for FL 60 will report beacon
> outbound

7.3.2   Arriving IFR flights operating outside controlled airspace shall request clearance from approach control to enter controlled or special rules airspace. Clearances will be given in a way similar to that in paragraph 7.3.1 above. In the examples below the initial approach fix is Stephenville NDB (or VOR), callsign SPV.

> Stephenville Approach
> Fastair 345

> Fastair 345 Stephenville
> approach pass your message

> Fastair 345 B737 25 miles
> south-west Stephenville IFR,
> FL 130 estimating zone
> boundary 20 SPV 24
> information charlie

> Fastair 345 cleared to SPV at
> FL 60. Enter controlled air-
> space south-west of Stephenville
> at FL 80 or below, no delay
> expected.

> Fastair 345 cleared to SPV at
> FL 60. Enter controlled air-
> space south-west of Stephenville
> at FL 80 or below

> Fastair 345 expect ILS
> approach runway 27 QNH
> 1014

> QNH 1014 request straight in
> approach Fastair 345

Fastair 345 cleared straight in approach report established on the localiser

Fastair 345 established on the localiser runway in sight

Fastair 345 number 1 contact tower 118.7

118.7 Fastair 345

Stephenville tower Fastair 345

Fastair 345 report outer marker

Fastair 345

Fastair 345 outer marker

Fastair 345 cleared to land wind 280 8

Cleared to land Fastair 345

Stephenville approach G-DCAB

G-DCAB Stephenville approach pass your message

G-DCAB PA 31 from Kennington IFR FL 80 estimate SPV 47 information Delta

G-AB cleared to SPV. Enter controlled airspace south-east SPV at FL 70. On reaching the SPV hold. Expected approach time 52

Cleared to SPV at FL 70. Enter controlled airspace at FL 70. At SPV enter the holding pattern expected approach time 52. G-AB

G-AB expect ILS approach runway 24

G-AB

G-AB revised expected approach time 1048

Expected approach time 1048 G-AB

G-AB descend to 3 500 feet QNH 1015

G-AB leaving FL 70 for 3 500 feet QNH 1015

G-AB cleared ILS approach runway 24 report outer marker outbound QFE 1009

G-AB ILS approach runway 24 QFE 1009

G-AB outer marker outbound

G-AB report established ILS inbound

G-AB

G-AB established
ILS inbound

G-AB report outer marker

G-AB

G-AB outer marker

G-AB contact tower 118.7

118.7 G-AB

Stephenville tower G-AB
outer marker

G-AB cleared to land wind
260 22

Cleared to land G-AB

7.3.3   On occasion IFR aircraft do not complete the instrument approach
procedure but request permission to make a visual approach.

Stephenville approach
G-ABCD

G-CD Stephenville approach

G-CD estimating SPV 49

G-CD cleared for an NDB approach runway 24 maintain 3 000 feet QNH 1011, no delay expected

G-CD NDB approach runway 24 3 000 feet QNH 1011

G-CD over SPV 3 000 feet VMC field in sight, request visual approach

G-CD cleared for visual approach runway 24 QFE 1005 contact tower 118.7

QFE 1005 118.7 G-CD

Stephenville tower G-ABCD long final, runway 24

G-CD Stephenville tower cleared to land runway 24 wind 250 10 QFE 1005

Cleared to land runway 24 QFE 1005 G-CD

7.3.4   Normally a holding procedure is published. However, the pilot may require a detailed description of a specific holding procedure.

Fastair 345 hold at North Cross FL 100

Fastair 345 request holding procedure

71

> Fastair 345 hold at
> North Cross FL 100 inbound
> track 265 degrees turns left
> outbound time 2 minutes
> EAT 1032

> Fastair 345 request
> holding procedure

> Fastair 345 hold on the
> 265 radial from Marlow VOR
> at 25 miles DME FL 100
> inbound track 085 degrees
> turn right EAT 1032

It should be noted that the above information is passed in the following order:

(a) Fix

(b) Level

(c) Inbound track

(d) Right or left turns

(e) Time of leg

7.4   **VFR ARRIVALS**

7.4.1   Depending on the procedures in use, the pilot of an arriving VFR flight may be required to establish contact with the approach control unit and request instructions before entering its area of jurisdiction eg before entering a special rules zone. Where there is an ATIS broadcast the pilot should acknowledge that he has received it; where no ATIS broadcast is provided the approach controller will pass the aerodrome data.

Stephenville approach
G-ABCD

G-ABCD Stephenville
approach

G-ABCD C172 from Walden
to Stephenville VFR at
2 500 feet estimating zone
boundary 52 Stephenville 02
information golf

G-CD route zone boundary
to Stephenville VFR QNH
1012, traffic information
there is a southbound
Cherokee 2 000 feet VFR
estimating zone boundary 53

QNH 1012 traffic in sight
G-CD

G-CD report aerodrome
in sight

G-CD wilco

G-CD aerodrome in sight

G-CD contact tower 118.7

118.7 G-CD

Note: The phraseology for joining the aerodrome traffic circuit is detailed in Chapter 4.

7.5   SPECIAL VFR FLIGHTS

7.5.1   Normally a special VFR clearance is only issued when requested by a pilot. The pilot of an aircraft on a special VFR flight –

(a)   must comply with ATC instructions;

(b)   is responsible for ensuring that his flight conditions enable him to remain clear of cloud, determine his flight path with reference to the surface and to keep clear of obstructions;

(c)   is responsible for ensuring that he flies within the limitations of his licence;

(d)   is responsible for complying with the relevant low flying restrictions of Rule 5 of the Rules of the Air and Air Traffic Control (other than the 1500 ft rule);

(e)   is responsible for avoiding aerodrome traffic zones unless prior permission for penetration has been obtained from the relevant ATSU.

7.5.2   A full flight plan is not required for Special VFR flight but the pilot must give brief details of the callsign, aircraft type and pilot's intentions. A full flight plan is required if the pilot wishes his destination to be notified.

7.5.3   Aircraft are not normally given a specific height to fly but vertical separation from aircraft flying above can be achieved by requiring the Special VFR flight to fly not above a specified level (Section (d) above must be borne in mind by pilots).

7.5.4   No separation can be provided between Special VFR flights which are flying in notified areas or routes where an individual clearance is not required, or between flights using such areas or routes and other flights on Special VFR clearances. Full details of the procedures for special VFR flights appear in the UK AIP, RAC, Section 1.

RADAR VECTORS TO FINAL APPROACH

7.6.1   Radar vectors are given to arriving flights to position them onto a
         pilot-interpreted final approach aid, to a point from which a radar-
         assisted approach can be made or to a point from which a visual
         approach is made. In the following example an identified aircraft
         inbound to Georgetown is given radar vectors to the ILS. (See
         fig 2.)

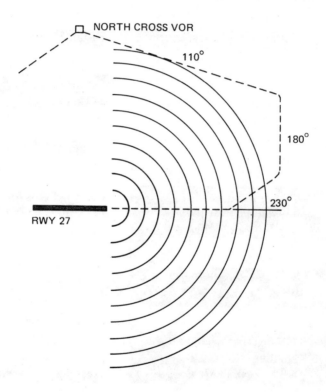

Fig 2   Radar vectored ILS approach

Georgetown approach Fastair 345 FL 60 approaching North Cross information Golf	Fastair 345 vectoring for ILS approach runway 27 QNH 1008
	QNH 1008 Fastair 345
Fastair 345 leave North Cross heading 110	Leave North Cross heading 110 Fastair 345
Fastair 345 report speed	Fastair 345 speed 260 knots
	Fastair 345 reduce speed to 210 knots
	Fastair 345 210 knots
Fastair 345 descend to 2 500 feet QNH 1008 number 4 in traffic	Leaving FL 60 for 2 500 feet QNH 1008 Fastair 345
Fastair 345 position 10 miles north-east of Georgetown	Fastair 345
Fastair 345 turn right heading 180 base leg, no ATC speed restrictions	Heading 180 Fastair 345

> Fastair 345 12 miles from
> touchdown turn right heading
> 230 closing localiser from
> the right report established

> Heading 230 ILS runway 27
> Fastair 345

> Fastair 345 established

> Fastair 345 descend on the
> ILS contact tower 118.9

> 118.9 Fastair 345

7.6.2   In the example above the approach speed of the aircraft is reduced
to maintain separation between aircraft in an approach sequence.
Where speed adjustment would be insufficient, it may be necessary
to issue additional vectors.

> Fastair 345 delaying action
> make a three sixty turn to the
> left

> Three sixty turn to the left
> Fastair 345

> Fastair 345 for spacing
> continue present heading
> taking you through the
> localiser

> Fastair 345

7.7   QGH PROCEDURE

7.7.1   QGH letdowns may be provided, when requested by a pilot, at aerodromes where the procedure is approved. The procedure provides for control of an aircraft from its initial approach altitude to a position from which an approach can be completed visually (see diagram at figure 3) this approach may not be aligned with a runway.

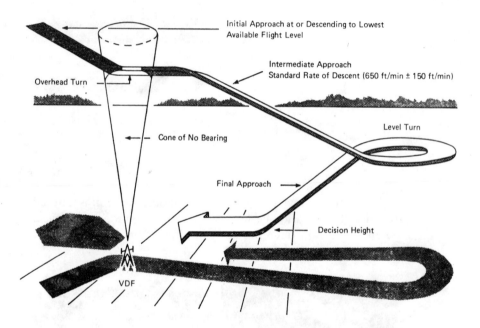

Fig 3   QGH procedure

7.7.2   On receiving a request for a QGH the aircraft is to be homed overhead the VDF aerial at or descending to the lowest available flight level. During homing the following message is to be passed to the pilot:

> G-ABCD this will be a QGH procedure
> Aerodrome QNH 1012
> Obstacle clearance limit 460 feet
> Check your decision height.

> QNH 1012, G-ABCD

7.7.3   During the procedure aircraft replies are used to obtain D/F bearings. Pilots may be asked to make additional transmissions for D/F. With some equipment the full callsign is sufficient to obtain bearings.

> G-CD transmit for D/F

> G-CD transmitting for D/F.
> One, two, three, four, five.
> G-CD

> or

> G-ABCD

7.7.4   Immediately the aircraft has passed overhead the VDF aerial, turn instructions are given to achieve the desired outbound track.

> G-CD D/F indicates that you have passed overhead. Turn left heading 095 degrees.
> Report steady

> Left 095 degrees. G-CD

79

7.7.5 On completion of the overhead turn and when bearings indicate the aircraft is outbound, heading corrections derived from a series of bearings are given by the controller as required to make good the desired outbound track. Descent instructions and the appropriate pressure setting are also given during this procedure.

> G-CD descend to 1 000 feet.
> QFE 1008. Report level

> G-CD 1 000 feet, QFE 1008.
> Will report level G-CD

7.7.6 On completion of the timed outbound leg (eg 3 min) the aircraft is given a turn onto a heading to achieve the final approach track.

> G-CD standby for inbound
> turn

> G-ABCD roger

> G-CD turn left heading
> 260 degrees, report steady

> 260 degrees, G-CD

7.7.7 When the aircraft reports steady on completion of the inbound turn, headings will continue to be given to achieve the inbound track. During the inbound leg the controller will pass instructions to be followed in the event of a missed approach. Descent clearance to decision height will be given on this leg.

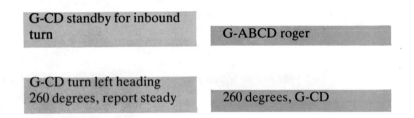

> G-CD in the event of a missed
> approach climb straight
> ahead to 2 000 feet, turn
> right and hold at the SPV

> Roger, G-ABCD

> G-CD report QFE set

> QFE 1008 G-CD

| G-CD descend to decision height. Report field in sight | Descend to decision height. G-CD |

7.7.8   If the pilot has not reported 'visual' by the time decision height is reached he may be instructed to maintain level flight until he is overhead the VDF.

If the aircraft is not 'visual' when overhead the VDF, the controller will give the instruction to carry out a missed approach procedure.

7.8   SURVEILLANCE RADAR APPROACHES

7.8.1   During a surveillance radar approach (SRA) the pilot is given distances from touchdown, advisory height information and azimuth instructions to enable him to make an approach to a particular runway. Controllers at civil aerodromes in the UK will normally pass advisory heights based on the QFE.

| Fastair 345 this will be a surveillance radar approach terminating at half a mile touchdown. Obstacle clearance limit.... feet | |
| Check your minima | Fastair 345 |

7.8.2   If a pilot wishes to conduct his approach by reference to altitude he must inform the controller and request the QNH. The controller, when passing the QNH, will add the aerodrome or touchdown elevation to the advisory heights. All references to the level of the aircraft will then be to altitude.

7.8.3   If the pilot reports visual in the early stages of the approach he will be asked whether he wishes to continue the SRA. Normally aircraft will not be transferred to aerodrome control until after they have landed.

7.8.4   The range at which the descent begins depends on the height of the aircraft during the intermediate phase and the angle of the glide path. The following example commences when the aircraft, having been descended to 2 000 feet QFE, is awaiting instructions for an approach on a three degree glide path.

Fastair 345 turn right
heading 275 final approach

Fastair 345 heading 275

Fastair 345 eight miles from
touchdown. Your descent will
begin at 6½ miles. Check
wheels

Fastair 345

Fastair 345 7 miles from
touchdown. Report runway
or approach lights in sight

Fastair 345

Fastair 345 approaching
6½ miles from touchdown.
Commence descent now to
maintain a three degree
glide path

Fastair 345 leaving 2 000 feet

6 miles from touchdown.
Height should be 1 850 feet

Fastair 345

Slightly left of track. Turn
right heading 280

heading 280 Fastair 345

5½ miles from touchdown.
Height should be 1 700 feet

Fastair 345

5 miles from touchdown.
Height should be 1 550 feet.
Heading 280 is good

Fastair 345

4½ miles from touchdown.
Height should be 1 400 feet.
Slightly right of track. Turn
left 3 degrees heading 277

heading 277, Fastair 345

4 miles from touchdown.
Height should be 1 250 feet.
Do not acknowledge further
instructions

(the gap between further transmissions will be less than 5 seconds)

3½ miles from touchdown.
Height should be 1 100 feet.
Cleared to land runway 27.
Surface wind calm.

3 miles from touchdown.
Height should be 950 feet.
Heading 277 is good.

2½ miles from touchdown.
Height should be 800 feet.
Heading 277 is good.

2 miles from touchdown.
Height should be 650 feet.
Check decision height.

1½ miles from touchdown.
Height should be 500 feet.
On track.

1 mile from touchdown.
Height should be 350 feet.

On track. Half a mile
from touchdown. Approach
completed. Out.

7.8.5   When the SRA terminates at 2 miles from touchdown the advisory
level checks at half mile intervals are omitted and pilots are
expected to reply to all transmissions from the ground station.

CHAPTER 8 – AREA CONTROL

8.1   AREA CONTROL UNITS

8.1.1   The following examples of phraseology are suitable for use at air traffic control centres according to the requirements of the prevailing traffic situation.

Fastair 345 request descent	Fastair 345 maintain FL 350 expect descent after Kateway
	Maintaining FL 350 Fastair 345
Fastair 345 descend to cross Wicken FL 170 or above, after Wicken descend to FL 130	Fastair 345 descending to cross Wicken FL 170 or above after Wicken descending FL 130
Fastair 345 are you able to cross Wicken at time 52	Fastair 345 affirm
	Fastair 345 cross Wicken not before time 52
	Fastair 345 wilco

8.2   POSITION INFORMATION

8.2.1   In order to assist in establishing separation, pilots may be instructed to provide additional position report information as well as routine reports.

Fastair 345 report Wicken	Fastair 345
	Fastair 345 Wicken 47 FL 350 Marlow 55
	Fastair 345 roger
Fastair 345 report 25 miles DME from Wicken	Fastair 345
Fastair 345 report distance from Stephenville	Fastair 345 37 miles
Fastair 345 report crossing radial 270 Wicken VOR	Fastair 345

8.3 LEVEL INFORMATION

8.3.1 Level information comprises climb and descent clearances or instructions and reports of leaving, reaching and passing levels as detailed in paragraph 3.2. When the word 'now' is used in a climb or descent clearance the aircraft is expected to vacate the level as soon as practicable. Under exceptional circumstances, if instant descent is required the word 'immediately' shall be used.

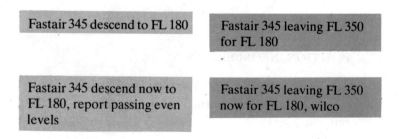

Fastair 345 descend to FL 180	Fastair 345 leaving FL 350 for FL 180
Fastair 345 descend now to FL 180, report passing even levels	Fastair 345 leaving FL 350 now for FL 180, wilco

| Fastair 345 descend immediately FL 200 due traffic | Fastair 345 leaving FL 220 immediately for FL 200 |

| Fastair 345 climb FL 220 report passing FL 100 | Fastair 345 climbing to FL 220 will report passing FL 100 |

8.3.2 An aircraft may request permission to leave controlled airspace by descent.

| Fastair 345 request permission to leave controlled airspace by descent | Fastair 345 cleared to leave controlled airspace by descent. Report passing 5 500 feet (Regional) QNH 1014 |

| | Fastair 345 leaving FL 70 will report 5 500 feet (Regional) QNH 1014 |

In the above example the base of the airways is 5 500 feet.

8.4 FLIGHTS JOINING AIRWAYS

8.4.1 Aircraft requiring to join an airway should make their request to the appropriate ATSU. Where no flight plan has been filed, the request should include the filing of an airborne flight plan (see Chapter 3). Where a flight plan has already been filed an abbreviated call may be made:

| Alexander control Fastair 345 request clearance to enter controlled airspace north-east of Marlow at FL 240 | Fastair 345 enter controlled airspace north-east of Marlow at FL 240 cleared to Georgetown beacon via Red One Seven to maintain FL 240 |

> Fastair 345 cleared to enter controlled airspace north-east of Marlow FL 240 cleared to Georgetown beacon via Red One Seven maintain FL 240

> Fastair 345 correct

8.4.2   Because of the prevailing traffic situation, a joining clearance may not be issued immediately.

> Fastair 345 remain outside controlled airspace expect joining clearance at time 55

> Fastair 345 remaining outside

8.4.3   In the event that the requested flight level is already occupied the controller will offer an alternative.

> Fastair 345 request FL 240

> Fastair 345 unable approve FL 240, FL 220 available

> Fastair 345 accept FL 220

8.5   FLIGHTS LEAVING AIRWAYS

8.5.1   Flights leaving controlled airspace will normally be given a specific point at which to leave, together with any other relevant instructions necessary to ensure separation.

> Fastair 345 cleared to leave controlled airspace north-east of Marlow maintain FL 230 whilst in controlled airspace

> Fastair 345 is cleared to leave controlled airspace north-east Marlow maintain FL 230 whilst in controlled airspace

8.6   FLIGHTS CROSSING AIRWAYS

8.6.1   An aircraft requiring to cross an airway should make its request to the appropriate ATSU.

Alexander control G-ABCD

G-ABCD Alexander control pass your message

G-ABCD C172 20 miles north of Wicken heading 220 FL 80 IMC Wicken at 33 request crossing clearance of airway A1 at Wicken

G-CD is cleared by Alexander control to cross A1 at Wicken maintain FL 80 whilst in controlled airspace

G-CD is cleared to cross A1 at Wicken maintain FL 80

G-CD report Wicken

G-CD wilco

8.7   FLIGHTS HOLDING EN-ROUTE

8.7.1   When an aircraft is required to hold en-route, the controller will issue holding instructions and a time at which onward clearance can be expected. Where it is not self-evident, the reason for the delay should also be given.

Fastair 345 hold at Wicken
FL 220, expect onward
clearance at 03, landing
delays at Georgetown
20 minutes

Hold at Wicken FL 220
Fastair 345 expect onward
clearance at time 03

CHAPTER 9–DISTRESS AND URGENCY PROCEDURES

9.1   INTRODUCTION

9.1.1   This chapter describes the characteristics of the VHF Aeronautical Emergency Service and the RTF procedures which should be used under the Aeronautical Mobile Service during an emergency. Additional information is published in the UK AIP (SAR and COM) sections and AICs.

9.2   VHF EMERGENCY SERVICE

9.2.1   Characteristics of the service

9.2.1.1   Within the United Kingdom, the Distress and Diversion (D & D) Cells at the London and Scottish Air Traffic Control Centres (LATCC and ScATCC) are assisted by suitably equipped civil and military ATSUs in the provision of an emergency service on the VHF International Aeronautical Emergency Frequency, 121.5 MHz. The service is continuously available to pilots in distress or in urgent need of assistance and to those who experience difficulties which could lead to a state of emergency.

9.2.1.2   The D & D Cells provide an emergency aid and fixer service and in respect of the latter they rely on information obtained by telephone from units equipped with VDF on 121.5 MHz. This procedure, and the necessity for manual plotting of the bearings received, will almost inevitably result in some delay in the provision of a fix by the Emergency Controller. The accuracy of VDF bearings, and hence the quality of fixes, depends on the height of the aircraft and its position relative to VDF stations. In general, the service is limited below 3000 feet amsl and, under such circumstances, the ability to assist a pilot who is uncertain of position will depend on the amount and accuracy of the information which can be given to the Emergency Controller regarding routeing and observed landmarks.

9.2.1.3   The ATSUs involved provide an emergency communications and aid service. Some, such as the RAF Military Emergency Diversion Aerodrome (MEDAs) maintain a continuous watch on 121.5 MHz but not all are equipped with VDF. Others do not normally listen out on 121.5 MHz but they have VDF and may be alerted by an ATCC to provide assistance.

9.2.2 Use of the service

9.2.2.1 Pilots are urged to request assistance from the emergency service as soon as there is any doubt about the safe conduct of the flight. The provision of assistance may be delayed if a pilot does not pass clear details of his difficulties and requirements.

9.2.2.2 When SSR is carried, a pilot experiencing an emergency whilst receiving an air traffic service should normally retain the mode and code setting required by ATC until instructions to the contrary are received. In all other situations, however, the transponder should be set to Code 7700 and Mode C.

9.3 DISTRESS

9.3.1 General

9.3.1.1 Transmissions from aircraft in distress have priority over all other transmissions. When a pilot is already in communication with a civil or military ATSU, assistance should be requested on the frequency in use; otherwise, a call should be made on the emergency frequency. If appropriate, and time permits, an aircraft equipped with the maritime distress frequency of 2182 kHz should transmit a distress message on that frequency in an effort to alert ships and coastal stations. (Certain North Atlantic Ocean Station vessels keep a listening watch on 121.5 MHz and this frequency must be monitored by all aircraft crossing the North Atlantic). If the pilot of an aircraft in distress elects to change frequency, he shall transmit on the frequency in use a short message indicating the frequency which he intends to change to.

9.3.1.2 On hearing a distress message, all stations must maintain radio silence on that frequency unless they themselves are required to render assistance and should continue to listen on the frequency concerned until it is evident that assistance is being provided. A distress message should normally be addressed to a specific ATSU, but it may be the subject of a general broadcast if time and circumstances make this necessary. The station addressed will assume control of the aircraft in distress but where the distress message is not acknowledged by the station addressed, or in the case of a general broadcast, any station shall respond immediately and either take control or alert another ATSU to the incident. The Emergency Controller at LATCC or ScATCC will normally answer calls on 121.5 MHz and, once communication has been established, pilots should not leave that frequency without the agreement of the Emergency Controller.

9.3.2   **Distress Signal**

The initial call or message relating to the immediate assistance required by an aircraft or vessel in distress should be prefixed 'MAYDAY' (preferably spoken 3 times on the initial call).

9.3.3   **Distress message transmitted by emergency aircraft**

A distress message transmitted by an aircraft in distress should, as far as time and circumstances permit, consist of the distress signal and the following information which, if possible, should be passed in the order given:

(a)   Name of station addressed (when appropriate)

(b)   Callsign and type of aircraft

(c)   Nature of the emergency

(d)   Intention of the person-in-command

(e)   Present position, flight level/altitude and heading

(f)   Pilots qualifications, eg:

  (1)   Student pilot;

  (2)   No instrument qualifications;

  (3)   IMC rated;

  (4)   Full instrument rating.

See Notes A & B on page 97.

Mayday mayday mayday
G-ABCD C172 engine fire
losing height intend an
immediate forced landing
20 miles south of Walden.
Passing 3 000 feet heading
360 PPL

G-ABCD Walden tower
roger mayday

Mayday mayday mayday
Walden tower G-ABCD C172
engine failed. Will attempt to
land Walden field, 10 miles
south, 4 000 ft heading 360
Student pilot

G-ABCD Walden tower
roger mayday cleared
straight-in runway 35
wind 260 10 knots QFE 1008
you are number one

9.3.4 Relayed distress message

Any aeronautical station or aircraft knowing of a distress incident
may transmit a distress message whenever such action is necessary
to obtain assistance for the aircraft or vessel in distress. In such
circumstances, it should be made clear that the aircraft transmitting
is not itself in distress.

Mayday mayday mayday
Walden tower G-ABCD have
intercepted mayday from
GBJQD I say again GBJQD
Cessna 172 engine failure
forced landing 10 miles
west of Wicken VOR,
1 000 feet descending,
heading 120 PPL, over

G-ABCD Walden tower
roger your relayed mayday
from GBJQD out

9.3.5 Imposition of silence

9.3.5.1 The aircraft in distress or the station in control of an emergency incident may impose silence either on all stations in the area or on any particular station that interferes with emergency transmissions. In either case, the message should take the following form:

> All stations Walden tower
> stop transmitting. Mayday

> or

> Fastair 345 stop transmitting.
> Mayday

9.3.5.2 The aeronautical station acknowledging a distress message on a particular frequency may consider it prudent to transfer other aircraft from that frequency in order to avoid any disruption of transmission from or to the emergency aircraft.

> Mayday G-BJCD all other
> aircraft contact Walden
> tower on 123.8 out

9.3.6 Cancellation of distress communications and RTF silence

9.3.6.1 When an aircraft is no longer in distress it shall transmit a message cancelling the emergency condition.

> Walden tower mayday
> G-ABCD cancel distress,
> engine restarted, runway
> in sight. Request landing

> G-CD cleared to land
> runway 35. Surface wind
> 320 6 knots

> Cleared to land runway 35
> G-CD

9.3.6.2 When an emergency incident has been resolved, the station which has been controlling the emergency traffic will transmit a message indicating that normal working may be resumed.

> Mayday all stations Walden
> tower time 03 distress traffic
> G-ABCD ended out

9.4 URGENCY

9.4.1 General

9.4.1.1 Urgency communications have priority over all other communications except distress and all stations shall take care not to interfere with such transmissions. The urgency message should normally be addressed to the station with which the aircraft was last in communication or in whose area of responsibility the aircraft is operating. However, as with the distress message, an urgency message may be the subject of a general broadcast where time and circumstances make this necessary.

9.4.2 Urgency signal

9.4.2.1 Any call or message transmitted by an aircraft or vessel concerning the safety of an aircraft or other vehicle, or of some person on board or within sight, should be prefixed 'PAN PAN' (preferably spoken 3 times).

9.4.3 Urgency message

9.4.3.1 An urgency message should, as far as time and circumstances permit, consist of the urgency signal and the following information which, if possible, should be passed in the order given:

(a)   The name of the station addressed (when appropriate).

(b)   The callsign and type of aircraft.

(c)   Nature of the urgency condition.

(d) Intention of the person-in-command.

(e) Present position, flight level/altitude and heading.

(f) Pilot qualification, eg:

   (1) Student pilot

   (2) No instrument qualification

   (3) IMC Rated

   (4) Full Instrument Rating

(g) Any other useful information.

Note:(A) There is no ICAO requirement to include pilot qualification in an emergency message. However, this information should be included whenever possible in UK emergency messages as it helps the controller to plan a course of action best suited to the pilot's ability.

(B) Pilots are invited to use the callsign prefix 'TYRO' when in communication with a military unit or the D & D Section of an ATCC to indicate lack of experience. Upon hearing this code word, military controllers will ensure that they do not issue instructions which the pilot may have difficulty in following.

9.5 DIFFICULTY

9.5.1 The emergency service is also readily available to pilots who find themselves in difficulty but whose circumstances do not warrant a distress or urgency call. Pilots in difficulty should contact the appropriate ATCC (Drayton Centre South of 55N; Scottish Centre North of 55N) on 121.5 MHz. The call should contain the information given at para 9.4.3(a) to (f).

9.6 PRACTICE EMERGENCIES

9.6.1 Pilots are encouraged to simulate emergency incidents (but not distress) on 121.5 MHz, to enable them to gain experience of the service provided and to give practice to the Emergency Controllers. Practice calls need not disrupt a planned flight or involve additional expense since the pilot can request diversion to his intended destination or suspend the exercise as necessary.

9.6.2   Simulated emergency calls are to be prefixed 'practice' and the initial call on 121.5 MHz should be brief eg 'Drayton Centre/ Scottish Centre, this is GXXXX, request practice pan'. Before calling, pilots are to listen out on the emergency frequency to ensure that no actual or practice emergency is in progress. The Emergency Controller will indicate acceptance of the practice by transmitting 'GXXXX this is Drayton Centre/Scottish Centre, continue with practice' and the pilot should then pass details in the normal manner. SSR Mode A Code 7700 is not to be selected during a practice emergency unless the setting is requested by the Emergency Controller.

CHAPTER 10 – TRANSMISSION OF AERODROME INFORMATION

10.1   METEOROLOGICAL INFORMATION

10.1.1   Meteorological information in the form of reports, forecasts or warnings is made available to pilots using the aeronautical mobile service either by broadcast (eg VOLMET) or by means of specific transmissions from ground personnel to pilots. Standard meteorological abbreviations and terms should be used and the information should be transmitted slowly and enunciated clearly in order that the recipient may record such data as is necessary.

G-CD Walden tower present weather wind 360 degrees 5 knots visibility 30 kms 2 oktas 2 500 feet QFE 1008

G-CD QFE 1008

Fastair 345 Stephenville approach wind 360 degrees 25 knots visibility 1 mile continuous moderate rain 8 oktas 600 feet QNH 1001

Fastair 345 QNH 1001 what is the temperature

Fastair 345 temperature plus 7

Fastair 345

10.2   RUNWAY VISUAL RANGE (RVR)

10.2.1   When transmitting the runway visual range the abbreviation RVR will be used without using the phonetic word for each letter, eg. RVR runway 27, 800 metres. The runway designator may be omitted if there is no possibility of confusion.

10.2.2   Where instrumented runway visual range (IRVR) observations are available, more than one reading may be transmitted.

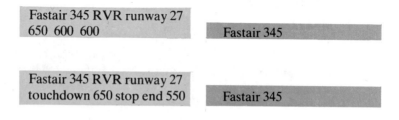

Fastair 345 RVR runway 27 650 600 600	Fastair 345
Fastair 345 RVR runway 27 touchdown 650 stop end 550	Fastair 345

10.3   RUNWAY SURFACE CONDITIONS

10.3.1   When conditions of standing water, with or without reports of braking action, are brought to the attention of a controller, the available information will be passed to aircraft likely to be affected.

10.3.2   Information on standing water will be passed in general descriptive terms, for example 'damp', 'wet', 'water patches' or 'flooded' according to the amount of water present.

10.3.3   When suitable equipment is available reports of braking action on wet runways will be passed to pilots.

10.3.4   Other runway surface conditions which may be of concern to a pilot will be passed by ATC.

Fastair 345 braking action medium .43, heavy rain time of measurement 0830	Fastair 345
Fastair 345 displaced threshold runway 27 500 feet due broken surface	Fastair 345

CHAPTER 11–MISCELLANEOUS FLIGHT HANDLING

11.1   WAKE TURBULENCE

11.1.1   When wake turbulence is suspected or known to exist ATC will warn aircraft as appropriate. Normally ATC will provide the spacing between aircraft but, if a pilot elects to execute a visual approach it is his responsibility for adequate spacing, although ATC will pass the appropriate distance.

> G-BJCD caution vortex wake
> the recommended spacing is
> ......miles

> G-BJCD

11.2   WIND SHEAR

11.2.1   When wind shear is forecast or is reported by aircraft, ATC will warn other aircraft until such time as aircraft report the phenomena no longer exists.

> G-CD caution wind shear
> reported at 800 feet
> 3 miles final runway 27

> G-CD Roger

11.3   DIRECTION FINDING

11.3.1   A pilot may request a bearing or heading using the appropriate phrase or Q signal to specify the service required. Each transmission shall be ended by the aircraft call sign. The direction-finding station will reply in the following manner:

(1)   the appropriate phrase or Q signal

(2)   the bearing or heading in degrees in relation to the direction-finding station

(3)   the class of bearing

(4)   the time of observation, if necessary

Stephenville tower G-ABCD request QDM	G-ABCD Stephenville tower QDM 090 degrees class bravo
	QDM 090 degrees class bravo G-ABCD

11.3.2   The accuracy of the observation is classified as follows:

Class A – Accurate within plus or minus 2 degrees

Class B – Accurate within plus or minus 5 degrees

Class C – Accurate within plus or minus 10 degrees

Class D – Accuracy less than Class C

11.4   AIRMISS REPORTING

11.4.1   An Airmiss Report should be made by any pilot flying in the United Kingdom Flight Information Region, the Upper Flight Information Region or Shanwick Oceanic Area when he considers that a risk of collision has been occasioned during flight by the proximity of another aircraft.

11.4.2   The initial report is made by RTF to the ATSU in communication with the aircraft except that if the controllers workload is such that he is not able to accept the report the pilot will be requested to file details after landing.

11.4.3   The Pilot's RTF report should commence with words 'AIRMISS REPORT' and should include the following items:

Aircraft Callsign

Position of airmiss

Aircraft heading

Flight level, altitude or height

102

Altimeter setting

Aircraft attitude (Level/climbing/descending/turning)

Weather conditions

Date and time (UTC) of the Airmiss

Description of other aircraft

First sighting distance and details of flight paths of reporting and reported aircraft.

11.4.4 RTF Airmiss reports are to be confirmed in writing within seven days of the incident to allow follow up action to be taken. (See UK AIP RAC Section.)

11.5 OIL POLLUTION REPORTING

11.5.1 Pilots sighting substantial patches of oil are requested to make reports by RTF to the ATSU with whom they are in communication or the appropriate FIS in order that action can be taken.

The RTF reports should contain the following:

'OIL POLLUTION REPORT'

... Time and date (if required) pollution was observed

... Position and extent of oil slick

...Name and nationality or description, including any distinctive markings, of any vessel seen discharging oil

... Tide, windspeed and direction

... Weather conditions and sea state.

Information on the following may also be included.

(a) Assessment of the course and speed of any vessel seen discharging oil.

(b) Whether any oil was observed ahead of the discharging ship, and the estimated length of the slick in her wake.

(c) The direction in which the oil was drifting.

(d) The identity of any other vessels in the immediate vicinity.

11.6 INTERCEPTIONS BY MILITARY AIRCRAFT – RTF

Pilots are warned that should they become involved in an interception by military aircraft they should follow the international procedures as detailed in the UK AIP RAC Section.

11.7 AIRCRAFT OPERATING AGENCY MESSAGES

11.7.1   Aircraft operating agency radio stations may only transmit and receive flight regularity and flight safety messages.

11.7.2   Flight regularity messages comprise the following:

(a)   Messages regarding the operation or maintenance of facilities essential for the safety or regularity of aircraft operation.

(b)   Messages concerning the servicing of aircraft.

(c)   Instructions to aircraft operating agency representatives concerning changes in requirements for passengers and crew caused by unavoidable deviations from normal operating schedules. Individual requirements of passengers or crew are not admissible in this type of message.

(d)   Messages concerning non-routine landings to be made by the aircraft.

(e)   Messages concerning aircraft parts and materials urgently required.

(f)   Messages concerning changes in aircraft operating schedules.

11.7.3   Flight safety messages include the following:

(a)   Messages originated by an aircraft operating agency, or by an aircraft, of immediate concern to an aircraft in flight.

(b)   Meteorological advice of immediate concern to an aircraft in flight or about to depart.

11.7.4   It is permissible for aircraft operating agency messages to be handled by the aerodrome communication facility provided this can be achieved without interference with its primary role and no other channels are available for the handling of such messages.

11.7.5   Public correspondence messages are not permitted on frequencies in the aeronautical mobile service.

INDEX

Abandoned take-off, 42
Advisory height, 81
Advisory level, 84
Aerodrome Air Traffic Services, 33-35
Aerodrome communication facility (messages), 105
Aerodrome control service, 1, 81
Aerodrome Flight Information Service (Officers) *see* AFISO's
Aerodrome information, 50
Aerodrome information, Transmission of, 99-105
Aerodrome traffic, 1
Aerodrome traffic circuit, 43
Aeronautical communication services, 16
   Aerodrome air/ground communications service, 16
   Aerodrome Flight Information Service (AFIS), 16
   Air traffic control service, 16
Aeronautical ground station, 17
Aeronautical mobile services, 1, 91, 99, 105
Aeronautical stations, 1, 16, 20
Aeronautical telecommunications, 27
Aeronautical Terminal Information Service *see* ATIS
AFISO's, 33-34, 39, 48
Agency radio stations, 104
Air-ground communication, 1
Air traffic, 1
Air traffic service complaints, 28
Air traffic services, 1
Aircraft attitude, 103
Aircraft callsigns, 17, 101-102
   Character callsigns, 17
   Radiotelephony designators, 17
   Registration marking, 17
Aircraft communications, 28
Aircraft heading, 102
Aircraft identification, 24, 31
Aircraft operating agency, 17
Aircraft operating agency (messages), 104
Aircraft operating schedules, 104
Aircraft parts and materials, 104
Aircraft radio faults, 28
Aircraft, Servicing of, 104
Aircraft station, 1
Airmiss reporting, 102
Airways, 22, 87
   Flight holding en-route, 89-90
   Flights crossing airways, 89
   Flights joining airways, 87-88
   Flights leaving airways, 88
Altimeter settings, 22, 103
Altitude, 1
Approach and landing, 38, 45-48, *see also* Final approach
Approach control, 65-84
Approach control unit, 66, 72

Approach radar control, 57
Area control, 85-90
Area control centre, 2
Arriving aircraft, 40
ATC route clearance, 65
ATIS, 43
ATIS broadcast, 37, 72
ATSU, 6, 20, 32, 87, 89, 91-93, 102-103
Automatic terminal information service, 2
Avoiding action, 61-63

Blind transmission, 2, 23
Broadcast, 2

CAA form CA 163, 28
CAA form CA 647, 27
Callsigns, 16, *see also* Aircraft callsigns
CAP, 90, 410, 452, iii
Civil Aviation Publications, *see* CAP
Clearance limit, 2
Clearance requirements, 20-23
Climb clearance, 86
Cockpit workload, 48
Communication failure, 23-24
   Air to ground, 6, 23-24
   Ground to air, 24
Communications, 6, 16-25
   Record, 6
Communications relating to direction finding, 7
Communications, Transfer of, 20
Communications watch, 6
Conditional clearance, 40
Conditional instruction, 40
Controlled airspace, 57, 66, 88
Corrections, 19

Decision height, 83
Departing aircraft, 40
Departure information, 34-35
Descent clearance, 86
Difficulty, Pilots in, 98
Direction finding, 101-102
Distress, 92-93
   Communications, Cancellation of, 95
Distress message transmission, 93
Distress messages, 7, 92
Distress procedure, 91-100
Distress signals, 93
Drivers, 51-53

Emergency aircraft, 93, 95
Emergency communications, 91
Emergency communications, equipment, 24
Emergency controllers, 91, 93, 98
Emergency messages, 97
Emergency transmissions, 95
Engine starting procedures, 34-35
Expected approach time, 2

Facilities, Maintenance of, 104
Final approach, 45-48, 75-77, *see also*
  Aerodrome traffic circuit, Approach
  and landing
Flight handling, 101-105
Flight holding en-route, 89-90
Flight identification, 17
Flight Information Service (FIS), 103
Flight level, 2, 102
Flight plans, 2, 32, 87
Flight regularity messages, 7, 104
Flight safety messages, 7, 104
Flights crossing airways, 89
Flights joining airways, 87-88
Flights leaving airways, 88
Forced landing, 94
Frequency changes, 22
Fuel wastage, 34

General phraseology, 29-32
General procedures, 9-22
Glide path, 82
'Go ahead', 53
'Go around', 48
Ground radio station, 17

Heading, 2
Heading instructions, 22, 57
Height, 2
Holding instructions, 89
Holding point, 35, 38, 53
Holding procedure, 71

ICAO Annex 10, iii
ICAO DOC. 4444-RAC/501/11, iii, 20
IFR, 27
IFR arrivals, 66-72
IFR departures, 65
IFR flight, 2
ILS approach, 75
Initial approach, 78
Initial approach fix, 67
Instrument approach, 48
Instrument approach procedure, 70
Instrument Flight Rules, *see* IFR
Instrument meteorological conditions, 3
Instrumented Runway Visual Range (IRVR),
  100

Landing roll, 49
Letdown procedure . . ., *see* QGH
Letters, Transmission of, 10-11
Level, 3
Level information, 86-87
Level instructions, 22, 29-31
Listening watch, 6
Local departure instructions, 41
Log-book, 6
Lower airspace radar advisory service, 27

Maritime distress frequency, 92
'MAYDAY', 93

Messages, Categories of, 7
  Aerodrome communication facility (mes-
    sages), 105
  Aircraft operating agency (messages), 104
  Aircraft operating schedules, 104
  Aircraft parts and materials, 104
  Aircraft, Servicing of, 104
  Communications relating to direction
    finding, 7
  Distress messages, 7, 92
  Facilities, Maintenance of, 104
  Flight regulatory messages, 7, 104
  Flight safety messages, 7, 104
  Meteorological advice, 104
  Non-routine landing, 104
  Passengers and crew, Requirements for,
    104
  Public correspondence messages, 105
  Urgent messages, 7, 96
Meteorological advice, 104
Meteorological information, 99
Meteorological messages, 7
Microphones, 9
Military Aerodrome Traffic Zones (MATZ),
  26
Military aircraft interceptions, 104
Military Emergency Diversion Aerodrome
  (MEDA), 91
Miscellaneous flight handling, *see* Flight
  handling
Missed approach, 48, 80
Missed approach procedure, 3, 81
Movement instructions, 51-52

Navigation, 61
Non-routine landings, 104
North Atlantic Ocean Station vessels, 92
Numbers, Transmission of, 11-13

Oil pollution reporting, 103

'Pass your message', 53
Passengers and crew, Requirements for, 104
Pilot complaints, 27
Planned flights, 98
Poor visibility, 39
Position information, 85-86
Position reporting, 31-32
Practice emergencies, 98
Practice pan, 98
Pre-departure manoeuvring, 38
Public correspondence messages, 105
Pushback, 35

Q signal, 101
QGH procedure, 78-81

Radar assistance, 63-64
Radar control, 60
Radar failure, 58

Radar identification, 57-58
Radar phraseology, 57-64
Radar vectoring, 3, 57-58, 60-61
Radar vectors, 75-77
Radio callsign, 25
Radio check, 25
Radio communications failure, 63-64
Radio silence, 92
Radiotelephony signals, 97
Read back requirements, 20-23
Receiver failure, 24
Relayed distress message, 94
Reporting point, 3
Route clearance, 22
RTF airmiss reports, 103
RTF channels, 32
RTF communication, 27
RTF procedures, 91
RTF reports, 102-103
RTF silence, Cancellation of, 95
Runway braking action
    Report by controllers, 100
Runway crossing, 53-54
Runway number, 41
Runway surface conditions, 100
Runway Visual Range (RVR), 3, 99

Secondary surveillance radar, 58-59, 92
    see also SSR
Separation, 60-61, 74, 77, 85, 88
Service, Hours of, 6
SOS, 93
Speech transmission, 9
Speed instructions, 22
SSR mode A Code 7700, 98
SSR operating instructions, 22
Silence, Imposition of, 95
Simulated emergency calls, 98
Standard words and phrases, 14-15
Straight-in approach, 44
Surveillance radar approaches, 81-84

Take-off, 21
Take-off clearance, 38, 41
Take-off procedures, 38-42
Taxi instructions, 35, 37
Taxiing manoeuvres, 20
Taxiing time, 47
Test procedures, 24

Test signals, 25
Test transmissions, 24
Time checks, 13
Time, Transmission of, 13
'Touch and go', 47
Touchdown, 82-84
Traffic circuit, 47, see also Aerodrome
    traffic circuit
Traffic information, 61-63
Transmitting techniques, 9-10
Typical left-hand circuit, 43
TYRO, 97

'Under radar control', 57
Urgency, 96-98
Urgency procedure, 91-100
Urgency signals, 96, 98
Urgent messages, 7, 96

VDF, 81
VDF aerial, 79
VDF bearings, 91
VDF information, 22
VDF stations, 91
Vehicle call sign, 51
Vehicle towing aircraft, 54-55
Vehicles, see Aerodrome air traffic services
Vehicles, Movement of, 51
Very High Frequency, see VHF
Very High Frequency Direction-Finding
    Station see VDF
VFR, 27, 48
VFR arrivals, 72-73
VFR departures, 66
VFR flights, 3, 66, 74
VHF, iv
VHF emergency service, 91-92
VHF International aeronautical emergency
    frequency, 91
Visual approach, 70, 75, 81, 101
Visual Flight Rules, see VFR
Visual inspection, 46-47
Visual meteorological conditions, 3
VOLMET, 99

Wake turbulence, 101
Wake turbulence, heavy, 18
Weather conditions, 103
Wind shear, 101

NOTES